YEAR GROUP PHOTOCOPIABLES

YEAR

5

Paul and Jean Noble

CREDITS

Authors
Paul and Jean Noble

Editor
Dulcie Booth

Assistant Editor
Gaynor Spry

Series designer
Lynne Joesbury

Designers
Paul Cheshire and Heather C Sanneh

Illustrations
Jon Sayer

Cover photographs
Manipulated images © PHOTODISC (globe, dice, magnet, paint brush, disk),
© DIGITAL VISION (hand), © STOCKBYTE (mask).

Published by Scholastic Ltd,
Villiers House,
Clarendon Avenue,
Leamington Spa,
Warwickshire
CV32 5PR
Printed by Bell & Bain Ltd, Glasgow
Text © Paul and Jean Noble
© 2003 Scholastic Ltd
1 2 3 4 5 6 7 8 9 0   3 4 5 6 7 8 9 0 1 2

Visit our website at www.scholastic.co.uk

British Library Cataloguing-in-Publication Data
A catalogue record for this book is available from
the British Library.

ISBN 0-439-98303-7

CONTENTS

INTRODUCTION

Every year in the primary school is preparatory and involves laying foundations for future learning and clearing paths for the next forward steps. Yet it does sometimes seem as though some years are more preparatory than others. Year 5 is such a year. In Year 5 we become acutely aware that the countdown to Year 6 SATs will soon be measured in terms rather than years and that there is still a lot to be done. We have even heard teachers remark that this is the year to panic, which is a pity, because Year 5 children can be a rewarding group to teach. They have sufficient learning, skills and maturity to take on increasingly interesting and challenging tasks and the quality of their interactions with adults has more depth and subtlety than before. They can be a pleasure to talk to and to teach, especially as their attitudes are generally unaffected by that pre-adolescent world-weariness that can taint Year 6s.

But there is a lot to be done. Partly because of the accumulation of work, which needs revision and partly because the National Curriculum marches ever onward. The pressure on teachers and children can be considerable, but it is certainly lessened if previous teaching has been thorough and has covered the ground prescribed. In terms of stages of learning, children are beginning to fan out across a wide field and differentiation of some activities may not always be sufficient to cater for children's needs. Some children will still need teaching at a Year 4 level, or even Year 3 or Year 2, and you will need to consider using material prepared for those year groups to cater for them.

We have relied heavily upon the Schemes of Work, drawn up by the Qualifications and Curriculum Authority, to help us make choices about what we include in this book because these schemes are the acknowledged basis for many school syllabuses (see www.qca.org.uk/ or www.standards.dfee.gov.uk/ schemes). Worksheets, like teachers, do not operate in a vacuum, for learning is a complex process that only works if there is intellectual activity, that is, the learner's brain has to be switched on. When you walk into a classroom, brains do not automatically go online, and when worksheets are handed out, intellectual activity is not automatically stimulated. (We would like to think that it happens sometimes.) You still have to engage the learner's mind, stimulate interest in the subject and, more often than not, set the context for the work, but that said, we are sure that you will find much to help you here and plenty that will challenge, amuse and satisfy your children. The *Year Group Photocopiables* series draws on substantial teaching experience and provides a readily accessible support,

particularly when you are limited by time or challenged by voracious learners. Supply teachers and others 'caught on the hop' will also be able to rely on this material to help them to cope with demanding days.

What the photocopiable sheets cover

This particular volume is based on the range of curriculum subjects and experiences that are described within *The National Curriculum: Handbook for primary teachers in England* (www.nc.uk.net). Inevitably, weighting has been given to the core subjects (English, mathematics and science) and the worksheets have been compiled bearing in mind the demands of the Literacy and Numeracy Strategies as well as QCA subject guidance. The non-core foundation subjects (design and technology; ICT; history; geography; art and design; music) except PE, are included but in varying degrees, depending upon the suitability of the content to the photocopiable format. Non-foundation subjects such as religious education, PSHE and citizenship are covered where subject matter allows. Of course the sheets neither tackle everything laid down in the government's pronouncements on the curriculum, nor everything in your school syllabuses, so they cannot constitute a complete curriculum. Rather like basic car insurance, the cover provided here is fundamental rather than comprehensive; a book that attempted to be comprehensive would be many times larger than this, as well as being difficult to justify in principle. Nobody wants children to overdose on worksheets.

The choice of content was made on the following grounds:

● Content and activities must translate sensibly into the photocopiable format. (Activities that are predominantly 'hands-on', colour dependent or oral have been largely avoided.)

● Activities must be worthwhile and interesting.

● Subject matter should relate directly to the prescribed National Curriculum.

● Content should satisfy some of the demands of the Numeracy and Literacy Strategies.

We have largely avoided providing repetitious sheets; instead we have favoured range of cover in order to keep the book to a manageable size. Suggestions for reinforcement and extension are included in the teacher's notes.

Using the material
Before using one of the photocopiable sheets, it is recommended that you read the teacher's notes that accompany it. These have been deliberately kept brief and contain four sections:

Objective
Every teaching objective is linked to curriculum guidance issued by the government. In maths and English, for example, the objectives match targets specified in the Numeracy and Literacy Strategies. Objectives have been stated in direct and unpretentious terms, but it is not claimed that a child doing a particular sheet will fully achieve that objective – we wish that teaching and learning were that easy.

What to do
This section provides notes on how the activity should be introduced and worked through with the children. These instructions repeatedly refer to the adult support that children will require and to the importance of talk and discussion. It is very important to get children to 'think out loud' as an aid to learning, but we have also made the assumption that children will be given oral instruction and support. Instructions given on the sheets are kept brief, although many children will now have reached a sufficient level of reading competency to cope with quite complex written instructions. The teacher's notes state when, and what, equipment will be required (usually very little), how the activity might be taught (whole class, group, individual instruction), and the degree of teacher support that is likely to be needed.

Differentiation
This section covers many strategies for differentiation, including: **modification** – we suggest that the sheet is changed in some way, instructions are omitted, language modified, or sections altered; **material**

support – help is suggested in the form of books, apparatus or equipment; **cooperative support** – solo activities are changed into group or paired activities where children can support each other; **adult support or intervention** – adults are required to supervise, interpret or help in some other appropriate way; **time allocation** – it is suggested that children are given more time to complete a task or are given more of the teacher's time; **by outcome** – different expectations may be held for particular groups of children (for example, some might give oral rather than written answers).

When you have opted to use one of the sheets you will have made a judgement that the activity is appropriate to the abilities of most of the class. If it is too difficult for some, first question whether this activity should be given to those children at all because if there is a marked mismatch between ability and task, then you should reject the task. (Perhaps some suitable activity will be found in an earlier volume in this series.) Where a task is too easy for a child, again you should first question the decision to use that sheet at all. In practice, an 'easy' task may be used as reinforcement of prior learning, but when a more able child completes such a task more rapidly and more accurately than the rest of the class, you will look to provide extra work to extend that child's learning.

Extension
This section suggests follow-up and extension activities. Extension activities can be used as a form of differentiation for more able children but they are mainly intended to provide some form of reinforcement to help achieve the objective. Apart from where particular apparatus or teaching is required, most of the extension activities could be completed at home. It is recommended that the issues being dealt with (including the support provided for parents), the value of completing the work at home and competing demands on the child all be undertaken before homework is set.

Progression
The order of the photocopiable sheets has been kept as logical as possible – it is expected the first sheet would usually be taught before the tenth sheet, for example. However, this order will not necessarily match the order of your teaching programme, and in some subject areas there is simply no obvious order for the teaching of particular activities. Nevertheless, a thread of progression runs through the book, and, more visibly, through the series. This is inevitable as the material is tied to a progressive National Curriculum. It does mean, however, that reference can be made, both forward and backward, for more or less challenging activities for the children to undertake.

ENGLISH

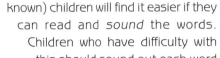

Conventions and rules make up a large part of the Literacy Strategy, although language is flexible and is much more than a collection of rules. It is therefore important that the rules are set in context. Similarly these worksheets should only be treated as part of a coherent language programme.

Using a sampling approach, we have aimed to cover a range of material and topics from the Literacy Strategy for Year 5, choosing our subject matter by sticking to the guiding principle of concentrating on what lends itself most readily to the worksheet format. Fortunately this left us with a great deal of work that could be tackled effectively; although you will find a distinct bias towards word- and sentence-level work and less emphasis on text-level work where comprehension and composition really demand stimulus and experience not readily compressed into a single sheet of A4. Perhaps more importantly, text-level work can also benefit greatly from adult intervention and social interaction.

Apart from *The National Curriculum* and the *National Literacy Strategy* themselves, further details of the Literacy Strategy teaching programme can be obtained by consulting other relevant government publications, in particular those published by the Standards and Effectiveness Unit. Although the range of some of these publications can be off-putting where they encompass more than one Key Stage, they do contain useful material within them. See, also, *The NLS Word Level Work, Activity Resource Bank, Module 2*, published jointly by DfES and OUP.

Letter strings (page 13)

Objective: To build up independent spelling strategies by using common letter strings.

What to do: First make sure that children understand what a letter string is. This is best done by example and could be part of direct instruction to the whole class. Then the sheet can be used as it is. The strings are *-ing*, *-ant*, *-ear* and *-ound*. The words should be matched to the correct balloons accordingly. You may wish to provide the children with separate pieces of paper on which to record their sentences, as there is insufficient room on the sheet for this.

Differentiation: Some of the words may be difficult for the children and although this may not apparently add difficulty to the exercise (meanings need not be known) children will find it easier if they can read and *sound* the words. Children who have difficulty with this should sound out each word to an adult first to make sure that they can hear the strings as well as see them. Dictionaries need to be available for the last part of the sheet.

Extension: Set children the task of adding to the collection of words in each balloon string. Identifying common patterns to aid spelling is the point of the exercise so encourage them to extrapolate from these given words to others. This could be set as a homework task.

i before e? (page 14)

Objective: To investigate and learn the spelling rule 'i before e except after c'.

What to do: You can use this sheet without preliminaries but you might like to set children the initial task of finding words with *ei* and *ie* in them. Write them on the board or flip chart. Do any patterns emerge? Spelling books, word lists and dictionaries will help children tackle this sheet.

Differentiation: Provide appropriate wordbanks and dictionaries for less able children to use. They might also benefit from working with a partner.

Extension: Ask children to practise spelling these words using the look–say–cover–write–check strategy. This could be a homework task followed by a spelling test in class.

Suffix towers (page 15)

Objective: To build up independent spelling strategies using common suffixes.

What to do: Revise the meaning of the term *suffix*. Unless there is difficulty in reading the instructions, children should be able to tackle this activity unaided although dictionaries and spelling books are, once again, useful support.

Differentiation: If children can identify and read the words and the suffixes, little differentiation should be needed although working with a partner will provide support for less confident children

Extension: Ask the children to create two more towers (a possible homework task) using *-ate* and *-able*. Get children to practise spelling these words (using the look–say–cover–write–check strategy).

Homophones (page 16)

Objective: To distinguish between homophones.

What to do: Children should quickly understand what is required although you could start with the sentence at the bottom of the sheet. Write it on the board or flip chart and ask children what is wrong with it. How can it be put right? The homophones are: pain/pane; pair/pear; sale/sail; bury/berry; thrown/throne; break/brake; ate/eight; plain/plane; hair/hare; stake/steak; rows/rose; prints/prince; stalk/stork; great/grate.

Differentiation: Although the spellings are quite simple some children may need to use a dictionary. Once again, this task is made easier if children work in pears (oops) – pairs.

Extension: Challenge children to write sentences like the one at the bottom of the sheet using the wrong homophones. Who can come up with the funniest sentence? Have a class competition. You could set this for homework so that Dad can have a go.

More than one: plurals (1)
(page 17)

Objective: To investigate, collect and classify spelling patterns in pluralisations and to construct rules for regular spellings.

What to do: Each collection of words should conform to the same rule on pluralisation. The rule is clearly given with each set of words. Instruct the children to sort the words given at the bottom of the sheet into the appropriate plural category. They should add more words of their own that conform to the rule to complete all the blanks.

Differentiation: Provide dictionaries and wordbanks for less able children.

Extension: Ask children to explain the rules on making plurals as if they were telling someone who did not

know the rules at all. This could be done orally (let a child give a 'lesson' to the class) or they could write out the rules as an entry in an encyclopedia. *What are plurals? How do you make them?* This could be a task for homework.

More than one: plurals (2)
(page 18)

Objective: To investigate, collect and classify spelling patterns in pluralisations and to construct rules for regular spellings.

What to do: This sheet is an extension of the previous sheet but covers three new rules. See notes above.

Differentiation/extension: See 'More than one: plurals (1)', above.

Idiomatic phrases, clichés and expressions (page 19)

Objective: To collect and classify a range of idiomatic phrases, clichés and expressions.

What to do: Most phrases like this do have some connection with their literal meaning and you might wish to explore this connection, for example 'playing with fire'. When children have grasped this idea they should be able to work out which meanings fit the idioms given. Make sure they understand that they choose an idiom and write it alongside the meaning on a separate piece of paper.

Differentiation: Solving word puzzles like this is easier if two brains are involved. Give those children who struggle the support of a partner.

Extension: Ask children to keep a 'sayings' diary for a week and record any idiomatic phrases that they hear used at home or in school. Can they write down their meanings? Children might like to explore dictionary definitions of the words *idiom* and *cliché*. Get them to look in several dictionaries. Can they write their own definitions?

Prefixes (page 20)

Objective: To collect and investigate the meanings and spellings of words using prefixes.

What to do: The key to this activity is the use of dictionaries. The meanings will come from the dictionaries, as will, of course, the words, so make sure that children understand how to find their way around one. A short revision lesson on alphabetical order would be useful. Play a speed game. *Who can be the first to find the word…?* It cannot be stressed too often that children must be given good equipment to work with. Check that your dictionaries are fit for the task.

Differentiation: Instead of requiring four words you

All change (I) (page 22)

Objective: To transform words by changing verbs to nouns using suffixes.

What to do: Adding suffixes is not just a case of sticking the suffix on the end; it often involves changes to the root words. Make sure that children understand this or you will get *pacifyism* instead of *pacifism*. Can they see why the *y* has been dropped in that case? (A double superfluous vowel.) The activity should otherwise be straightforward. Tell the children they need to write the words on the spokes in the correct wheel.

Differentiation: Provide dictionaries for those who need them, especially to check meanings when they are writing the sentences. This will be challenging for some children and you may wish to make it a group activity.

Extension: Can children add to the spokes of the wheel? This is a challenge. It is not that easy to think of new examples. Children need to write the verb and the noun.

All change (2) (page 23)

Objective: To transform words by changing nouns to verbs using suffixes.

What to do: See the previous sheet, 'All change (I)'.

Differentiation/extension: See 'All change (I)', above.

Auxiliary verbs (page 24)

Objective: To recognise how different tenses are formed using auxiliary verbs.

What to do: We suggest that you let children use highlighter pens but underlining with coloured pencils is cheaper and probably less likely to cause a mess. Revise what a verb is (the children should not have trouble with this). Direct children to spot the main verb first (which is easiest), the auxiliary verb should then be easy to spot. The auxiliary verbs in the sentences are: **1.** could, **2.** has, **3.** will, **4.** may, **5.** were, **6.** was, **7.** was, **8.** shall, **9.** have, **10.** are.

Differentiation: Differentiate by not setting this activity for children who do not confidently recognise verbs. For less able children you might highlight all the verbs and ask them simply to choose those that are auxiliary.

Extension: Set a page from a book (their library book perhaps) and ask children to copy and mark sentences that contain auxiliary verbs. This could be a homework task if a suitable text is used (check first).

From now to tomorrow (page 25)

Objective: To investigate how future tenses are formed using auxiliary verbs.

What to do: Check children understand *future* and

can make the task easier by asking for one word in each section only. Children should work on this activity on their own but you should keep an eye on less able children to make sure that they are using the dictionaries correctly.

Extension: Challenge children to write a sentence containing as many words with prefixes as they can. It must make some sort of sense! For example, *It was nearly **im**possible but I **trans**lated the **tele**phone conversation in very **in**convenient **circum**stances.* This could be a homework puzzle.

Onomatopoeia (page 21)

Objective: To explore onomatopoeia and to collect, invent and use words whose meaning is represented in sounds.

What to do: Children are usually quick to catch on to onomatopoeic words (they love the word itself). Give a few examples. *Bang* on the table! *Clap* your hands! Make sure they understand that they are to invent some new words as part of the activity.

Differentiation: This is a good activity for less able children because it involves spelling new (invented) words using sounds that they know as well as known words. Let them work in pairs and use a dictionary if you find that this is really necessary.

Extension: Ask children to write a poem, a song or a piece of prose containing lots of onomatopoeic words. Alternatively you might ask them to find a verse of a poem that contains the most onomatopoeic words as a class competition. Add the word *onomatopoeia* to the class spelling test!

present. Answers: **1.** Flo will be a very good ballet dancer. **2.** Raji will live in Solihull. **3.** Arnold will be on holiday in Cyprus (or will be going to). **4.** She will eat roast beef. **5.** Mona will enjoy her skiing lessons. **6.** Gandulf will become a very fat dog (or will be).

Differentiation: Ask children to imagine that everything that is described in the sentences will happen tomorrow. How would the sentence be phrased then? If necessary, tell less able children to start each sentence with the word *tomorrow*.

Extension: Ask children to write a paragraph describing what they (and their family) will be doing during the school summer holidays.

From one person to another
(page 26)

Objective: To identify and classify examples of 1st, 2nd and 3rd person from reading.

What to do: Telling one person from another takes a bit of practice. Demonstrate how the grid can be used to help. Take some examples from a newspaper or a book, apply the grid and tell children how to express the answer, for example *2nd person singular*. Answers: 3rd person plural, 2nd person singular (it could be plural but in the context of the nursery rhyme there was only one!), 3rd person plural, 3rd person singular, 2nd person plural and 1st person singular.

Differentiation: It is easier if you underline the nouns and pronouns and direct children to find them on the chart and work out the answers from there.

Extension: Play a game of 'spot the person'. In turn, children stand up and say a sentence. The class then work out in which 'person' the person is speaking. For example, *On Saturday we went to town to buy new shoes.* (1st person plural.) *My cousins all have motorbikes.* (3rd person plural.)

Direct speech – reported speech (page 27)

Objective: To be able to recognise and write direct speech.

What to do: One of the easiest ways for children to check and learn the rules is to find direct speech as it is printed in a book. (Choose the book with care.) Make sure that the children place the appropriate full stops, commas, question marks and exclamation marks before the inverted commas and not after. Answers: 'Ding, dong!' chimed the clock. The Prince shouted, 'Don't go, Cinderella!' 'I never go to the Ball,' moaned the footman. 'I think that the Prince is very, very handsome,' twittered the bird. 'Am I really a pumpkin?' asked the coach. Cinderella said, 'I wish that I had worn my trainers.'

Differentiation: This should be accessible to most reasonably competent readers. Group the less confident readers together with an adult 'narrator' to help with any difficult text and do it as a group activity.

Extension: Cartoons can be used to provide further practice where the text is suitable.

Reported speech – direct speech (page 28)

Objective: To understand the difference between reported speech and direct speech.

What to do: Explain the activity. Explain to the children that their answers may not all be precisely the same as there are sometimes choices that can be made. For example, you could write Cinderella 'wondered whether' or 'wondered if' as both are correct and you could also put information in a different order. Answers (allow small variations as described): Cinderella wondered whether she should clean and cook or marry the Prince. The Ugly Sisters shouted at the Fairy Godmother to leave their pumpkins alone. The Fairy Godmother asked whether she should turn the Ugly Sisters into toads. The footman moaned that he didn't have a fairy godmother.

Differentiation: This can be tackled as a group exercise, like most problem solving it is easier that way. The group need only have one scribe.

Extension: Collect examples of reported speech, perhaps from a local newspaper. Enlarge them and display them in class.

Directions for dialogue (page 29)

Objective: To understand how dialogue is set out.

What to do: There is a lot of text here and it may be a good idea to read it as a class exercise. Why do we need all this complicated punctuation? (It should be obvious when you start reading the piece without punctuation.) Reiterate the rules. Children should write this on a fresh piece of paper as this will need space. It is easiest to mark this directly rather than refer to an 'answer' sheet.

Differentiation: Cutting the piece in half will make the task more manageable for less able children.

Extension: Challenge the children to continue the dialogue to a satisfactory end. This would make a good homework task.

Writing a script (page 30)

Objective: To write a playscript applying conventions and adding production notes.

What to do: Explain a few of the conventions of playwriting. They do not have to be too detailed at this stage but they should name players who are speaking, use colons after their names and make simple notes on the production (lighting, noises off stage, and so on). The latter can be put into brackets. Explain that playscripts do not use speech marks. Show children simple playscripts so that they can see what is required. Allow children to develop this 'playlet' beyond the text given if you wish. Remind them that they can continue their work on further sheets of paper.

Differentiation: Once again, this activity is easier if made a cooperative one.

Extension: Act out the play. Appoint a producer, actors and stage manager. Use one of the children's scripts. *What problems does the producer encounter? How could the script be improved?* Children could rewrite their plays after this activity to improve and extend the scripts.

Writing for radio (page 31)

Objective: To write a playscript applying conventions and adding production notes.

What to do: This sheet is intended to stimulate the children's imagination. Direct them to follow the instructions on the sheet and underline the fact that the play is for radio. What sound effects do they need to add? What about introductory music? Talk to the children about making a plan first so that they know how the play is going to end. Get them to think about the beginning, middle and the end. They will need to write their playscripts on a separate sheet of paper.

Differentiation: An adult might lead a discussion session to plan out the plot, as some children will have difficulty here. You may wish to give children a start by providing the opening dialogue.

Extension: Children could work in groups to produce and record their plays on tape. This could be an ongoing activity over a period of time. They might also design programmes for the play using the illustrations provided and perhaps working on a word processor. They could also write reviews of the plays.

Points of view (page 32)

Objective: To present a case, setting down arguments as bullet points.

What to do: Find some official document with bullet points (we are sure that they are abundant in school) and show children how and why they are used. Explain to them how the paragraph on the photocopiable sheet contains information but no single point of view. Ask the children to decide whether or not they think the speed bumps are a good idea and to argue their case using bullet points to note down the main arguments. Stress that they can go beyond the information supplied if they have other points to make that are relevant.

Differentiation: Talk to less confident children and discover what their views are and then assist them to get started. Once they have their first bullet point the rest will follow more readily.

Extension: Turn the bullet points into a letter, a speech, a campaign poster and so on. Have a class debate – let the children take sides. Present a TV debate with an interviewer (it could be the teacher) questioning two people from each side of the argument.

Persuasive devices (page 33)

Objective: To collect and investigate the use of persuasive devices.

What to do: This is not easy. You will need to take one of the examples and talk the children through it. What is the person trying to do when they say that *only a fool would believe...?* (Saying that if they don't agree with him they must be stupid.) It may be best to have this sheet as an ongoing assignment over a period of time (say a week) and let children listen for and look for other examples of persuasive devices.

Differentiation: Clearly difficult (only a fool would think otherwise), so wise teachers will undoubtedly let children work with partners on this one. We cannot believe that you would do anything else.

Extension: This activity will work best over a period of time. Ask children to tell you whenever they hear you use a persuasive device. (You could regret this!)

Getting it wrong (page 34)

Objective: To explore ambiguities that arise from sentence contraction.

What to do: Make sure that the children understand the jokes in the cartoons. You will also need to explain the meaning of *ambiguous*. If they don't, you will need to explain them and the joke will be lost and possibly the understanding of ambiguity too! Emphasise that it is the shortening of sentences and phrases that causes the ambiguities to arise.

Differentiation: This activity readily lends itself to being a paired activity. You may find that enlarging the sheet makes drawing the cartoons easier.

Extension: Children will enjoy looking for more ambiguities like this. Ask them to collect such phrases over a few days. *Who can collect the most?* You might choose a headline (suitably ambiguous) from a newspaper and have a competition for the best foolish cartoon based on this.

A pile of prepositions (page 35)

Objective: To identify prepositions and to understand and use the term.

What to do: Refer first to the pile of prepositions. Explain what they do (define the relationship between nouns and pronouns) by reference to the examples. *What is the relationship between the bone and the chair?* The preposition *under* tells us. The list of prepositions is not exhaustive and children may like to add more that they find. Ask them to highlight or underline the preposition in the sentences. All answers can be found in the 'pile'. Answers: **1.** off, **2.** in, **3.** towards, **4.** over, **5.** down, **6.** against, **7.** through, **8.** to, **9.** behind.

Differentiation: Direct less able children to look at the two emboldened words in each sentence. Ask how they are connected. This should give them the answer. Remind them that all the answers are in the pile. They could check off each one as they are used.

Extension: Set children a suitable section of text to analyse for prepositions. Can they add to the pile?

I protest! (page 36)

Objective: To write a letter to protest or put forward a point of view.

What to do: Two things need to be done before letting children loose on this sheet. First make sure that they understand the conventions of letter writing. Show them a few genuine examples. Talk about the variations. In the computer generation there are usually fewer commas and full stops, especially in addresses. The modern style is to keep the text as clean as possible. Nevertheless, there are still conventions that all well-written letters observe. Show these to the children. Secondly, you should revise the strategy of organising an argument. Children could use bullet points (see earlier sheet) or make notes of the main points before they start writing. Ask them if they think they will need to use any persuasive devices in their letters. (See 'Persuasive devices', above.) They don't have to write against the proposed rubbish tip but ask those children not against it why, and this may spark off a class debate.

Differentiation: Differentiation will be by outcome in this instance. You should expect a coherent, well-argued letter from the more able children. Most children should make a clear case and all should display that they have grasped the essential details.

Extension: Take the opportunity to let children write a letter 'for real' when the occasion arises. It might be to the local newspaper or to the headteacher or a local councillor on an issue about which they feel strongly. Thank-you letters and letters seeking information are also good practice. There is no reason why this activity should not involve the use of ICT.

Letter strings

● Each word below contains a letter str**ing** (as in th**ing** and s**ing**le). There are four different letter strings in these words. Find them and underline them.

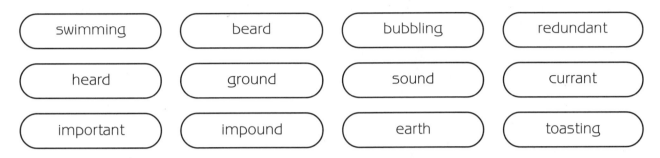

swimming	beard	bubbling	redundant
heard	ground	sound	currant
important	impound	earth	toasting

● Now write each string in the middle of a balloon, then add the words to the correct balloon strings!

● Put each word into a sentence to show its meaning.

i before e?

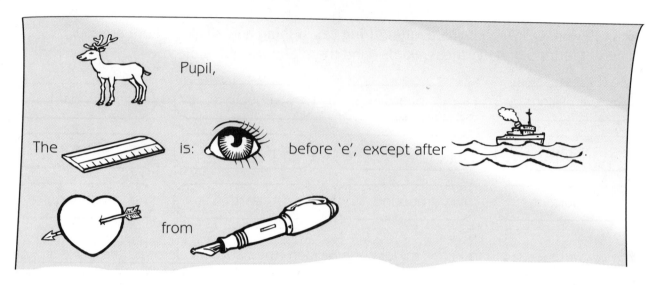

Pupil,

The [ruler] is: [eye] before 'e', except after [ship].

[heart with arrow] from [pen]

● Learn the rule: **i** before **e** ⟶ except after **c**

br**ie**f _____ _____	rec**ei**ve _____ _____
th**ie**f _____ _____	conc**ei**t _____ _____
fr**ie**nd _____ _____	c**ei**ling _____ _____

BUT

These words do not follow the rule:

their	_____	_____	_____	_____
heir	_____	_____	_____	_____
weird	_____	_____	_____	_____

● Use dictionaries and spelling lists to add to each group of words. How many can you add?
● Choose three words from each group and write a sentence to show their meaning.

Suffix towers

● Use the suffix at the base of each tower to build word towers as tall as you can. Can you find enough words to reach the top?

A **suffix** is a group of letters fixed to the end of a word and common to many words, for example **-ion**: perfection, selection, sensation, suspension.

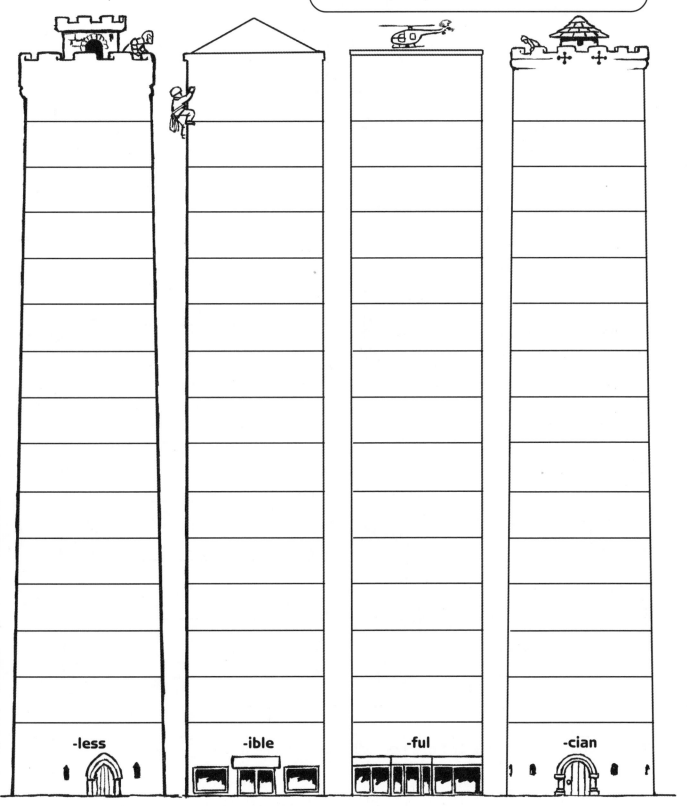

-less

-ible

-ful

-cian

● Check your words in a dictionary.

Homophones

here hear

some sum

son sun

road rode

> **Homophones** are words that sound the same but are not spelled the same and have different meanings.

● Find the homophones. The pictures will help you.

pain _____

pair _____

sale _____

bury _____

thrown _____

break _____

ate _____

plain _____

hair _____

stake _____

rows _____

prints _____

stalk _____

great _____

● Write out this sentence but use homophones to make it make sense.

My sun road to the beech to sea the sure.

_____

More than one: plurals (1)

To make a word plural, for most words add **s**:

| chairs | tables |

curtains

cars

For most words ending in **s**, **sh** or **ch**, add **es**:

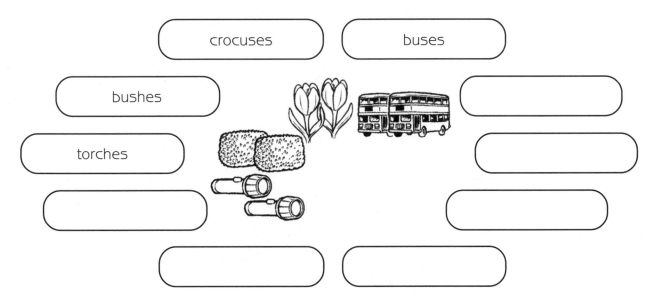

| crocuses | buses |

bushes

torches

Put these words in their correct group above by making them into plurals. Can you add any more? Use a dictionary to help you.

sink   marsh   stitch

flower   church   cat

More than one: plurals (2)

Change **f** to **ves**:

thieves   knives   wives

When **y** is preceded by a consonant, change to **ies**:

babies   ponies

parties

jellies

When **y** is preceded by a vowel, add **s**:

toys   boys

keys

donkeys

Put these words in their correct group by making them into plurals. Can you add any more? Use a dictionary to help you.

curry   half   life   monkey

day   daisy   tray   hoof

Idiomatic phrases, clichés and expressions

● Match up the phrases with their meaning (write them out on a separate piece of paper). Use them in writing whenever you can.

Phrase	Meaning
smell a rat	in the same circumstances
throw in the towel	behave better
sit on the fence	give up
mind your ps and qs	have nothing to do
take forty winks	be like your father
out of sorts	avoid taking sides
hang your head	good enough
turn over a new leaf	suspect something
act the goat	misunderstand the situation
a chip of the old block	behave foolishly
at a loose end	be careful about the way you behave
play with fire	feel ashamed
keep the pot boiling	have a short sleep
in the same boat	risk serious trouble
up to the mark	not feeling yourself
taken for a ride	carry on with what you are doing
past his prime	be deliberately misled
barking up the wrong tree	no longer at his best

● Can you think of any other idioms or expressions?

Prefixes

● Use a dictionary to find the meaning of these **prefixes**. Then find four words that begin with the prefix.

meaning

in- _____not_____ _____inactive, inexpensive, inaccurate, insufficient_____

im- _____ _____

ir- _____ _____

il- _____ _____

pro- _____ _____

sus- _____ _____

● Take one word from each group and write it in a sentence to show its meaning.

_____

_____

_____

_____

_____

_____

● Do the same with these prefixes. Write your sentences on the back of the sheet.

auto- _____ _____

bi- _____ _____

trans- _____ _____

tele- _____ _____

micro- _____ _____

Onomatopoeia

Onomatopoeic words sound the same as the action or sound being described. For example, a horse **neighs**.

● Add to this collection of onomatopoeic words.

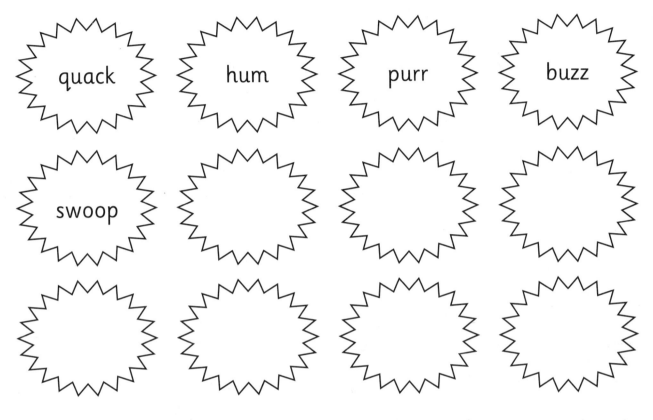

quack

hum

purr

buzz

swoop

● Invent some onomatopoeic words of your own.

● Use your onomatopoeic words in sentences.

_____

_____

_____

_____

All change (1)

● Change these **verbs** to **nouns** by adding one of the **suffixes** from the wheels. Write the new word on the spoke of the correct wheel. One has been done for you.

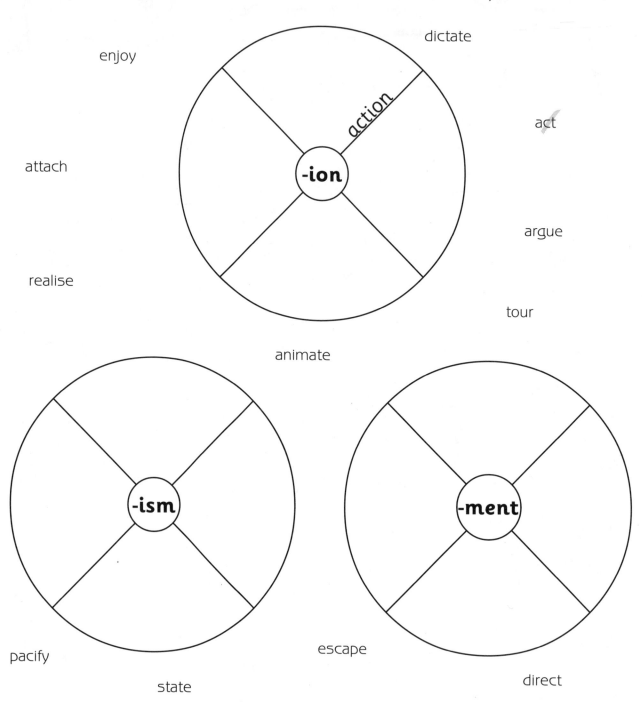

● Choose one word from each wheel and write a sentence to show its meaning.

_____

_____

_____

All change (2)

● Change these **nouns** to **verbs** by adding one of the **suffixes** from the wheels. Write the new word on the spoke of the correct wheel.

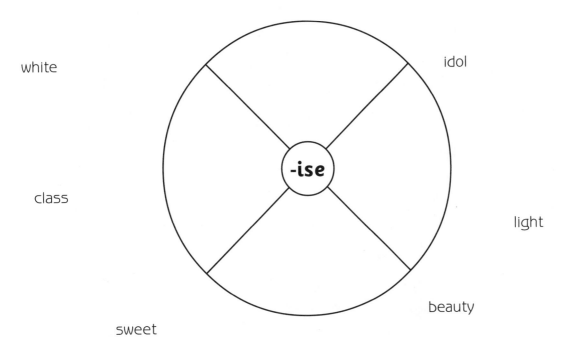

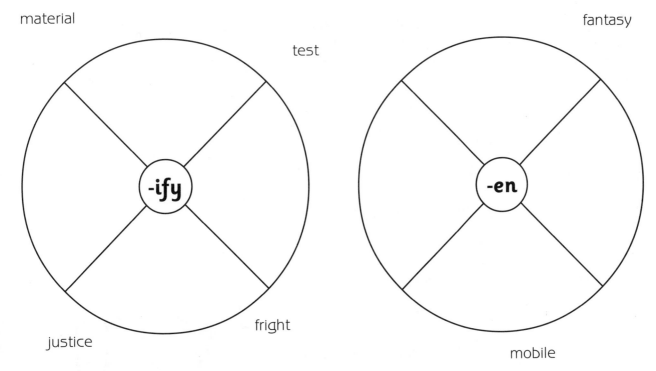

● Choose one word from each wheel and write a sentence to show its meaning.

_____

_____

_____

Auxiliary verbs

Grandma **was flying** to America.

auxiliary   main verb

Use a marker pen to highlight the **main verb** in each of these sentences. Can you see that there is another (auxiliary) verb in the sentence? Highlight the **auxiliary verbs** in a different colour. Study the example above before you begin.

1. Perhaps we could bake a cake tonight?

2. Fido has eaten too many Alabama mud pies.

3. We will grow old one day.

4. Margaret may come to your birthday party.

5. They were all running towards us.

6. Zimbabwe was called Rhodesia.

7. The Post Office was named Consignia.

8. I shall write a letter of complaint to the Mayor.

9. They have built the tallest tower in the world.

10. We are going on a steam train.

From now to tomorrow

When we write about something that is to happen in the future we often need an extra (auxiliary) verb as well as the main verb to get the tense right. For example:

I **shall fly** to Canada.	**fly**	main verb
	shall	auxiliary verb

They **will eat** fish on Friday.	**eat**	main verb
	will	auxiliary verb

Change these verbs using an auxiliary verb so that the sentences describe something that will happen in the future.

1. Flo is a very good ballet dancer.

_____

2. Raji lives in Solihull.

_____

3. Arnold is on holiday in Cyprus.

_____

4. She is eating roast beef.

_____

5. Mona is enjoying her skiing lessons.

_____

6. Gandulf is a very fat dog.

_____

From one person to another

	singular	plural
1st person	I	we
2nd person	you	you
3rd person	he, she, it	they

Use the chart above to work out which person the sentences below use. For example:
We are three little maids from school. (1st person plural)

sentence	person
 When will they ever learn?	
 Baa baa Black Sheep, have you any wool?	
 They charged into the Valley of Death.	
 Nasser scored 100 runs against India.	
 Do you all sing in the choir?	
 I am going to bed now.	

Direct speech – reported speech

To write direct speech you must use inverted commas and the words actually spoken. For example: "Let me try on the glass slipper," said the Ugly Sister.

Use direct speech to complete these sentences correctly. The first one is done for you.

"Ding, dong!" chimed the clock.

The Prince shouted,

_____ moaned the footman.

_____ twittered the bird.

_____ asked the coach.

Cinderella said,

Reported speech – direct speech

To write reported speech you do **not** use inverted commas or all of the words actually spoken. For example:

D   "Will you try on the glass slipper, Cinderella?" asked the Prince.

> **R**   The Prince asked Cinderella to try on the glass slipper.

Try writing reported speech for yourself.

D   "Shall I clean and cook or marry a prince?" wondered Cinderella.

> **R**

D   "Leave our pumpkins alone!" shouted the Ugly Sisters at the Fairy Godmother.

> **R**

D   "Shall I turn the Ugly Sisters into toads?" asked the Fairy Godmother.

> **R**

D   The footman moaned, "I haven't got a fairy godmother."

> **R**

Directions for dialogue

When we write down **dialogue** (speech involving more than one person), we need to keep certain rules.

- Use speech marks around the words actually spoken.
- Start a new line when a different person speaks.

For example: "Can you see England yet?" asked Pete the pilot.
"It's too cloudy to tell," replied Benji the navigator.

Write out this conversation keeping to the rules.

Judging by the instruments, Pete the pilot remarked, we don't have much fuel left. You always worry too much replied Benji the navigator sitting behind him. According to my calculations we are only 200 miles from base. I am sure we can make it. But the pilot continued to worry and did not remain silent for long. I think we ought to make for Brize Norton airfield Pete said after a few minutes. Oh no Benji exclaimed. Brize Norton is a long way from my home and I left my Ferrari in the car park at Gatwick. If we run out of fuel you won't even be driving a roller skate responded Pete angrily. You could let me jump out joked Benji. My mum would love to see me arrive home by parachute. I'll throw you out if you aren't quiet threatened Pete.

Writing a script

Playwrights write playscripts. A playscript:
- shows who says what
- includes production notes for the producer.

Turn this story into a play. Write who says what and provide stage directions. It has been started for you.

Script	Production notes
Police officer: Ullo, ullo! What's going on here?	Broken bike on floor
Zoe:	

Writing for radio

Write a short playscript for a radio programme. You must use the props, characters and setting shown below. (You can add extra if you wish.) Plan your plot first. Write out the dialogue and include production notes.

Props

Setting

Characters

Molly the Maid   Lord Arthur   Lady Arthur   Chief Inspector Noble   Roger the Robber

Points of view

Because there had been quite a lot of accidents in Beechcroft Road, the council erected some speed bumps. Not everyone approved of them. One man crashed his car into a tree the day after they were built because he swerved after failing to see them. Some residents complained about the noise caused by vehicles braking as they approached the bumps. One mother wrote to the newspaper to say that the road was much safer for children now. An ambulance driver said that the bumps caused him to lose time when he was racing to an emergency. Someone complained about the cost of making them. Fast drivers seemed to enjoy swerving around the bumps as fast as they could. In the six weeks since they were installed no pedestrian has been hurt in a road accident.

Are speed bumps good or bad?

Decide what your point of view is and list your arguments as bullet points:

-

-

-

Persuasive devices

Tick – tick – tick – tick

We have ways of making you tock!

● When people want to win an argument they sometimes use all sorts of persuasive tricks and devices. Have you heard or read these phrases?

1. Clearly the truth is…

2. Only a fool would believe…

3. Every right-thinking person…

● Can you explain what these phrases are trying to do?

1. _____

_____

2. _____

_____

3. _____

_____

● Find some more examples. Collect phrases from your reading, from advertisements and so on.

Getting it wrong

Newspaper headlines, notices and labels often shorten sentences to save space. This can make their meaning ambiguous. Look at these examples.

● llustrate these showing that you have got the meaning wrong.

Police arrest man with golf club	Parking for mother and child
Holidays in the sun!	Smith thrashes the champion!

A pile of prepositions

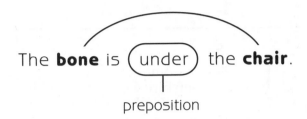

The **bone** is (under) the **chair**.

preposition

The preposition **under** shows how the nouns **bone** and **chair** relate to each other.

Here is another example:

They **jumped** (across) the **puddle**.

They and **puddle** are related by the preposition **across**.

Highlight the **prepositions** in these sentences.

1. It rained, and the **water** dripped off her **nose**.

2. She put her **head** in her **hands** and cried.

3. The **osprey** dived towards the **sea**.

4. They tripped over the **dog**.

5. The **chickens** ran down the **road**.

6. A few exhausted **firefighters** were resting against the **wall**.

7. "Put the **key** through the **letterbox**!" shouted the woman.

8. Without stopping, **he** drove to **Truro**.

9. She kept the **money** behind the **cornflakes packet**.

by   down

for   back

to   behind

with   through

around   off

against   up

over   on

from   in

towards

I protest!

The Planning Officer
Barsetshire County Council
County Hall Buildings
Rumsey Road
Barset
BT1 4PN

The Headteacher
Sunshine Primary School
Meadow Flower Lane
Cuddlecombe
Barsetshire
BT27 5XG

20th July 2003

Dear Headteacher

This letter is to inform you that the council is building a
refuse disposal facility at the end of your school's
playing field. It will be state of the art, so noise and
smell will be kept to a minimum. Between 4 and 15 lorries
an hour will deliver to the site at peak times but there
will be no deliveries on Sunday (although the bulldozer
will operate then). The council will doubleglaze your
offices to keep out the noise and put a high wire fence
around the playground to catch the rubbish blown by the
wind.

Unfortunately we will need to use part of your football
pitch for the access road but we will compensate you
financially.

I am sure that you will welcome this facility as it will
benefit the residents of the village because it is cheaper
to dump their rubbish here than in the quarry at Moorend.

Yours faithfully

N. O. Brain

N. O. Brain
Planning Officer

MATHS

The mathematics curriculum continues to move forward in Year 5 and although there is a great deal of consolidation of previous work, new ground is still being broken. For the first time children are introduced to the basic language of probability, need to cope with using a protractor to measure angles, start to use calculators efficiently, and begin to exhibit a considerable degree of sophistication when dealing with graphical presentations of data. So in spite of the looming threat of future SATs, Year 5 is far from being a year solely for mathematics revision.

In the following sheets we have gone for *range of cover* in regard to the National Numeracy Strategy, rather than comprehensive or in-depth provision, both of which would be impossible within the scope of this book. Most basic number-crunching, pencil-and-paper calculations and the like, are extensively and thoroughly covered in good primary maths textbooks, so we have made the not unreasonable assumption that you will have access to these, although we have tried to underpin work on notoriously weak topics (such as division). We have included some sheets introducing the use of calculators and there are also plenty of calculations to be made in topics like area and problem-solving. We have chosen to ignore maths that you might readily do orally or 'on the blackboard' on the whole, for obvious reasons. However, there are many useful ideas here that will provide sound backup for your basic maths teaching and support a range of objectives identified in the Numeracy Strategy for Year 5 children.

If you require an overview of the mathematics programme for Year 5, then refer to the key objectives summarised in thirteen bullet points compressed into half a page in chapter two of the Numeracy Strategy (page 4). The government has been a particularly prolific author on the subject of mathematics, so you can get further information from the following (and subsequent) publications (published by the DfES): *The National Curriculum* and (1) *The Framework for Teaching Mathematics*, (2) *Mathematical Vocabulary*, (3) *Teaching Mental Calculation Strategies*, (4) *Standards in Mathematics*.

Taking temperatures (page 44)

Objective: To use negative numbers in the context of temperature.

What to do: First ask the children to record the temperatures a to e. You may wish to check that they know how to go about reading a scale. Note that every degree is marked. Children should have come across negative numbers in Year 4 but you might also need

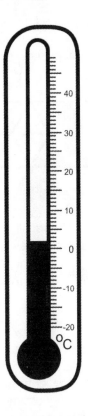

to revise this aspect of the sheet. Answers: **1a.** 2°C, **1b.** –6°C, **1c.** –15°C, **1d.** 14°C, **1e.** 12°C, **2.** in order: –15°C, –6°C, 2°C, 12°C, 14°C, **3.** 29°C, **4.** 8°C, **5.** 6°C, **6.** 10°C.

Differentiation: Size does make a difference and enlarging the thermometers will make it easier for less able children to count the divisions without error. Less able children will probably count the differences in temperature which others might calculate.

Extension: If you have suitable thermometers (Thermostik or maximum and minimum) and conditions are right, you can ask children to record and graph night-time and daytime temperatures. Alternatively, do the same with the lowest overnight temperatures taken from the TV weather forecast for the British Isles. You might give children arithmetic to work out on their calculator, with negative answers, so that they become familiar with the appearance of negative numbers on a calculator.

All square (page 45)

Objective: To recognise square numbers and relate to drawings of squares.

What to do: You might demonstrate how the square numbers can be built up by starting the grid on a board or flip chart. It is advisable to tell children to use two colours only for colouring the squares, for example red for the first square number, add blue for the second square number, add red for the third square number, add blue for the fourth and so on. The completed table will show all the square numbers from 1^2 to 10^2 (1, 4, 9, 16, 25, 36, 49, 64, 81, 100). The other answers are 81, 81m² and 25. The last question is a matter for your judgement.

Differentiation: Most children should manage this activity but you should insist that less able children record each calculation on the table below *as* each number is coloured on the grid, otherwise they will create a pretty pattern and may not be able to unravel the progression of square numbers from it. Others should be able to fill in the chart after they have coloured in the whole grid. You can let children use square counters or bricks to create a more solid representation of the progression of square numbers. The same sequence of numbers can also be created using triangular grid paper, building from one triangle to the next smallest congruent triangle and so on. Record the number of triangular 'bricks' from which the sequence is built and the square number sequence is again revealed.

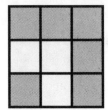 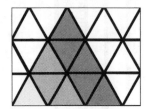

Extension: Ask children to discover and learn all the square numbers from 1^2 to 20^2. (A possible homework task.) Can they use a calculator to find square numbers? Is there more than one way of doing this?

For every... (page 46)

Objective: To solve simple problems involving ratio and proportion.

What to do: This sheet introduces the common language of ratio so it is worth doing a number of similar questions orally with the whole class first. For example, *In class 5 there are two girls for every boy. There are 11 boys in the class, how many girls are there? In every packet of ten wine gums there is one black one. How many black wine gums in eight packets?* Encourage children to tackle the problems on the sheet 'thinking out loud'. They can record their thinking on the sheet.

Differentiation: These sorts of problem are much simplified if they can be rendered 'concrete'. Let children who struggle with these questions use counters, bricks or any simple apparatus to represent the quantities in the problems.

Extension: Ask children to devise and illustrate three 'ratio' questions of their own. These can then be swapped around the class for other children to find solutions. This is a possible homework task.

Decimals, fractions and percentages (page 47)

Objective: To recognise the equivalence between percentages, fractions and decimals and to identify a percentage of a shape.

What to do: This question presumes that children have been introduced to decimals, fractions and percentages in practical contexts (for example, money, shopping, test scores, sharing in daily life, and so on). The chart to be learned is printed in full below. Make sure that the children's work has been marked and is correct before they memorise the equivalents. The

shaded percentages are: **a.** 25%, **b.** 20%, **c.** 10%, **d.** 50%, **e.** 75%, **f.** 50%, **g.** 50%, **h.** 75%.

fraction	decimal	%
1	1.00	100%
$\frac{1}{2}$	0.5	50%
$\frac{3}{4}$	0.75	75%
$\frac{1}{4}$	0.25	25%
$\frac{1}{5}$	0.2	20%
$\frac{1}{10}$	0.10	10%
$\frac{1}{100}$	0.01	1%

Differentiation: For those who cannot comprehend the numerical relationships here, you should make the activity into something more concrete. Use apparatus and games such as fraction boards and decimal/percentage dominoes. You can, of course, simplify the task by eliminating one column of equivalents, for example fractions.

Extension: Challenge children to find percentages of money and measures. For example, *What is 50% of one litre? What is 25% of £120?* Pose the questions in the fraction version as well, for example, *What is half of a litre? What is a quarter of £120?*

Leftovers (page 48)

Objective: To understand the idea of a remainder and to begin to give a quotient as a fraction when dividing by a whole number.

What to do: If you have not dealt with the problem of what to do with the remainder in a division sum then you should do so. Children need to understand that sometimes we will record the remainder as a fraction, sometimes as a decimal ($261 \div 10 = 26.1$) and sometimes ignoring it when it is sensible to do so, for example 13 children divided into two teams (neither 6.5 nor 6½ children makes sense). Children should record their answers on the sheet. Answers: **a.** $4\frac{1}{8}$, **b.** $5\frac{5}{6}$, **c.** $9\frac{4}{5}$, **d.** $12\frac{1}{6}$, **e.** $2\frac{4}{7}$, **f.** $6\frac{3}{4}$, **g.** $4\frac{7}{8}$, **h.** $12\frac{1}{3}$. The problem answers are **1.** 7 boxes, **2.** 4 coaches, **3.** 5 tickets.

Differentiation: Encourage children to see a fraction as a division sum, for example $1 \div 2 = \frac{1}{2}$ so a remainder of 5 when a number is being divided by 9 should be $5 \div 9 = \frac{5}{9}$. Let children use counters and so on to carry out the division sums if necessary.

Extension: Generate division sums on a calculator and ask children to 'round' their answers so that they are sensible in a familiar context. For example, money needs to be rounded to two decimal places: £45 ÷ 7 = 6.4285714 but recognise that the answer lies between £6.42 and £6.43 with £6.43 being the closest amount.

Estimate and calculate (page 49)

Objectives: To develop mental calculation strategies; to develop calculator skills and to begin to use a calculator effectively.

What to do: This is not a 'guess the answer' game. Encourage children to develop a variety of strategies that will help them to make sensible estimates. For example, 5 x 555 = the last digit of the answer must be 5 (question 1) because 5 x 5 = 25 therefore 2775 must be the correct answer from the selection of numbers given. Again, 405 ÷ 9 will be more than 405 ÷ 10 (question 5) but not substantially so. The sensible choice would be 45. Rounding up or down may also help hence 91 x 91 = 90 x 90 = 8100 (question 19), so the most sensible answer is 8281. Answers: **1.** 2775, **2.** 2592, **3.** 8982, **4.** 64, **5.** 45, **6.** 25, **7.** 378, **8.** 868, **9.** 1558, **10.** 36, **11.** 24, **12.** 17, **13.** 3960, **14.** 3124, **15.** 2890, **16.** 24, **17.** 64, **18.** 62, **19.** 8281, **20.** 3198, **21.** 5115.

Differentiation: Allow some children to use calculators from the start if estimation is beyond them. You could ask them to multiply the last digits only (or divide the first two or three). Can they get any clues from this? You might wish to withhold calculators from other children until their estimates have been recorded. Challenge more able children to do the task against the clock.

Extension: Ask children to devise ten multiplication sums of a similar sort, with three alternative answers (including the correct one) for a friend to solve. This might be a homework task.

Hot shot! (page 50)

Objectives: To develop calculator skills and to begin to use a calculator effectively; to reinforce understanding of place value.

What to do: A primitive form of the old 'Space Invaders' game, this can still be good fun and challenging for some children. Subtracting each digit requires an understanding of HTU place value – the game is very good reinforcement for this concept – and the children will also get plenty of practice at operating a calculator. An example is included on the sheet, shooting down the number 5472. You will need to provide plenty of paper for recording each 'shoot'.

Differentiation: Differentiation is best done by allocation of time. Allow children very unfamiliar with calculators to play with them and not be 'shown how' too eagerly. If there are problems with place value then you should revise the topic. Children might write down each number in its constituent parts before shooting, for example 5472 = 5000 + 400 + 70 + 2 then they can see clearly which numbers to subtract.

Extension: More practice is the best extension to this sheet. You can vary the game by asking children to shoot down numbers in size order starting with the biggest number. You might also add two places of decimals where children have sufficient experience to cope with this.

Polyominoes (page 51)

Objectives: To solve mathematical problems or puzzles; to recognise and explain patterns and relationships; to generalise and predict.

What to do: You can introduce the idea of polyominoes in a number of ways. Play with square islands and establish the rules (edge fully to edge, rotations and flip-overs are not 'new' arrangements). How many different-shaped dominoes are there? Examine the language. Where have we met the prefix *poly-* before? When exploring for arrangements of pentominoes, children can use the squares from the pentomino on the paper as a template and cut out the squares. Alternatively, give children squared paper to play with (expensive!). Some will be perfectly capable of sketching their arrangements on blank sheets but they will need to be organised as it is easy to repeat shapes without realising it (especially if they are rotations). There are 12 pentominoes. They approximate to the shapes of the letters FILPSTUVWXYZ.

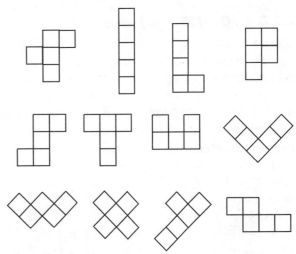

Differentiation: Handling the shapes does make the activity easier so let less able children make each shape as they go along. It is less easy to miss a repetition.

Extension: There are many extension possibilities. Can they work out the area of each polyomino? What are the perimeters of each shape? Are they unchanged for each set of polyominoes? How many hexominoes are there? You can make a set of pentominoes out of stiff card and use an 8 x 8 board with squares of the same size as the pentomino squares. Play a game in pairs. Each player chooses a piece in turn and tries to be the last player to lay a piece on the board. Another challenge is to see if children can fit all of the pentominoes onto the board.

It's a problem (1) (page 52)

Objective: To use all four operations to solve word problems involving numbers based on 'real life'.

What to do: You do not want children to pluck answers out of the air and it is important that they explain and record how the problem was solved using numbers, signs and symbols. There is, of course, no single 'correct' way of doing this, but you might choose to demonstrate how to solve a similar problem thinking out loud and recording your thoughts. Ask children to practise doing this in front of the class. Answers: **1.** one hour and 35 minutes, **2.** two hours and 20 minutes, **3.** 213 miles, **4.** 378 miles.

Differentiation: Some children will need extra attention. It is useful to get children (any children, but particularly the less mathematically competent) to talk through their answers to an adult. They will often recognise errors without prompting when they do this.

Extension: You cannot have too much practice at this sort of thing. One approach is to give children a sheet of problems on Monday morning and allow a short time (registration time?) for them to work on the sheet each day. Can they solve all the problems by Friday? Thursday? It's a challenge! Do this frequently and it is surprising how quickly children improve.

It's a problem (2) (page 53)

Objective: To use all four operations to solve word problems involving numbers in 'real life'.

What to do: See 'It's a problem (1)' above. Answers: **1.** 35.2kg, **2.** £13, **3a.** £204, **3b.** £43.25, **3c.** £64, **3d.** £4.80, **3e.** £66.50, **3f.** £36. **4.** Yes, they can all go. (They could take up to 85 people legally.)

Differentiation/extension: See above.

Know your measures (page 54)

Objectives: To use the vocabulary related to measures; to know and use the correct abbreviations for measures and to know relationships between familiar units; to know the names of commonly used imperial units.

What to do: You should talk about imperial measures and different systems of measuring. The picture at the top of the sheet demonstrates how we still use imperial measures. Ask children if they have heard any other different measures being used (for example, half a pound of cheese, 75°F, 6 feet tall). *Where did these measures come from?* Children will be familiar with miles and so on but probably not with the equivalencies. Children do need to be able to write and spell the names correctly so when the sheet is complete you may wish them to copy the statements out for memorising. Answers: distance, capacity, capacity; **1.** 4.74m, **2.** 32.51m, **3.** 1.4l, **4.** 5.5l, **5.** 4.3kg, **6.** 6.5kg.

Differentiation: Help children to memorise by playing guessing games and so on. Make a set of cards with abbreviations on one side and the full word on the other. Play with a group. Hold up the abbreviation. The first one to give the full name correctly keeps the card. The winner collects the most cards.

Extension: From an AA road atlas, or similar, give the children distances in miles for them to convert roughly into kilometres. Similarly, ask them to work out roughly how many kilometres their family car, or your car, does to the gallon. This could be a possible homework task.

Using the right measure (page 55)

Objective: To suggest suitable units to estimate or measure length, mass or capacity; to record readings from scales with a suitable degree of accuracy.

What to do: The sheet is self-explanatory and the answers in the speech balloons should be reasonable. It is easier to say what they should not be (for example, you wouldn't measure a fish in miles or litres; millimetres, centimetres, metres, or even inches would be acceptable).

Children should colour in the water levels in the containers. Answers: **a.** 360ml, **b.** 460ml, **c.** 430ml, **d.** 11cm 3mm (11.3cm or 113mm), **e.** 3cm 8mm (3.8cm or 38mm), **f.** 12cm 1mm (12.1cm or 121mm).

Differentiation: Let less able children replicate each of the liquid measures (you should possess identical or similar measuring equipment). They should measure the quantities for real but you may still need to support them by having adult help nearby especially when handling a ruler to measure the lines.

Extension: Challenge children to draw a series of lines of a precise length (a good homework task). It is important to give children practical experience of reading scales on measuring containers so set up some examples in the classroom, similar to those shown on the sheet, for the children to read and to record their measures.

Calculating areas (page 56)

Objective: To calculate the areas of rectangles.

What to do: You should point out that these drawings are not full size, they are scaled down to fit onto the paper. Encourage children to show their thinking and calculations on separate paper using appropriate measures and signs. Answers: **a.** 12m², **b.** 11m², **c.** 5m², **d.** 48cm², **e.** 25cm², **f.** 48cm², **g.** 132cm², **h.** 28cm², **i.** 16cm².

Differentiation: Children should have grasped the relationship between the dimensions of a rectangle and its area but for those who haven't, encourage them to mark in the squares on the rectangles. You should talk about the length by breadth relationship with them and lead them to calculate their answers.

Extension: Children in Year 5 are expected to be able to express the formula for working out the area of a rectangle in words. Challenge them to write down a coherent method for finding the area of any rectangle, using their own words. The use of letters to represent the words should be dealt with as a class lesson, if at all (it is required at Year 6).

Area and perimeter (page 57)

Objective: To measure and calculate the area and perimeter of simple shapes.

What to do: Make sure that children are using decent rulers that are in good condition for this sheet. They can write their answers on the sheet, next to the relevant shape. Children are expected to work out the areas by counting and approximating. They should colour in each square as it is counted. The answers are (accept an approximately correct answer for the area and perimeter of shape V): areas, T = 26cm², V = 33cm², E = 40cm² and H = 46cm²; perimeters, T = 30cm, V = 36cm, E = 44cm, H = 50cm.

Differentiation: Measuring the areas and perimeters of T, E and H is obviously fairly straightforward but the sloping letter V could pose problems. You could ask children to use a different coloured pencil for each side and then to add up the measurements of each differently coloured length.

Extension: Give children cm² paper and ask them to draw two letters of the alphabet in a similar style (say, A and F). Then measure area and perimeter as before. This is a good homework task.

The right time (page 58)

Objective: To read the time from timetables and to be able to understand and use that information.

What to do: It is intended that the cartoon figures be cut out and stuck onto the correct clock. Children will need to know how to read a 24-hour clock so this may need revising. Children should show their working out on paper. Answers: **1.** 32 minutes, **2.** 05:33 from Oxford, **3.** 10:27, **4.** four trains (the 09:51 doesn't run on Saturdays), **5.** no.

Differentiation: Provide apparatus in the form of digital clocks that can be manipulated easily. Let those that need this support use the clocks to count on the minutes between each time.

Extension: Ask children to collect a local timetable (bus or train) and bring it to school. They should devise a problem for a friend to solve using their timetable, for example *When is the last train to Bognor Regis?*

Missing links (page 59)

Objective: To name and describe 2-D shapes and to classify them according to their properties.

What to do: Explain to children that they should read the description on the left and match it to a shape with those properties on the right. The answers are, of course, on the sheet and the sheet is best marked by visual reference.

Differentiation: Some children will find this activity easier if they work in pairs. You could cut out the descriptions and shapes and ask them to match them physically. It helps if these shapes and their names are displayed in the classroom as the children will gradually become familiar with their properties.

Extension: Give children sets of shapes to classify. (You should have plenty of such shapes available in the classroom. They are available commercially in plastic and card, or can be home-made.) They could sort them into sets according to whether they are regular/irregular; sort triangles according to right-angled/isosceles/equilateral; and so on. Set children a challenge for homework, such as finding something that is heptagonal (for example 50p), hexagonal or trapezoidal.

Making reflections (page 60)

Objective: To recognise reflective symmetry in 2-D shapes, reflections and translations.

What to do: The language of symmetry is important and you should make sure that children know and can use that language, for example *reflection, translation, symmetry, symmetrical, axis of symmetry* and *reflective symmetry*. It is a good idea to introduce the topic by asking children to investigate the number of axes of reflective symmetry in regular and irregular polygons. This can be done using prepared shapes and a mirror. Paper shapes can also be folded to check for the axes. There is space provided for the children to draw the reflections by the shapes. The answers for **5** and **6** are:

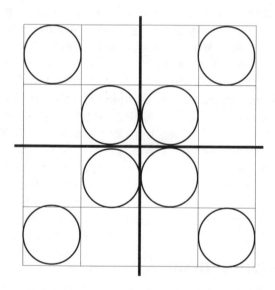

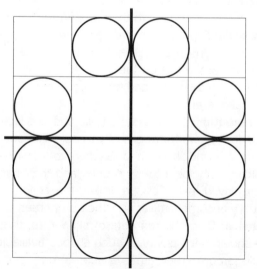

Differentiation: Provide mirrors or reflective sheets for children to test out their ideas before drawing.

Extension: The last two questions can be reset in similar style on a larger grid (say, eight squares by eight squares). These are the questions that children have difficulty with, so provide extra practice.

Coordinated shapes (page 61)

Objectives: To read and plot points using coordinates in the first quadrant; to recognise and identify parallel and perpendicular lines.

What to do: If necessary, revise how to plot coordinates before setting this task. The sheet is fairly straightforward and can be marked most easily by visual reference. The two shapes that the children should plot on the grid are a rectangle and an isosceles triangle.

Differentiation: The main problem is likely to be posed by getting the ordered pairs correct. Play games of tic-tac-toe to re-establish the rule (x before y – in at the door before going up the stairs). Some children may benefit by working co-operatively on this task.

Extension: Challenge children to list ten examples of lines, faces or edges that we meet in everyday life that are parallel/perpendicular. Children are sometimes fascinated by the idea that parallel lines meet at infinity. Where is that?

Measurement by degrees (page 62)

Objectives: To measure and calculate acute, obtuse and right angles in degrees; to use a protractor and to calculate angles in a straight line.

What to do: Use a large classroom protractor (if you have one) to demonstrate how it should be used. Make sure that all the protractors you use are not chipped and are clearly marked. (Some schools prefer to use circular rotating 'angle indicators' that are available commercially.) Remind children that the paper can be moved or rotated to suit their position, because the angle does not change. Make sure that they set themselves up properly to measure each angle Emphasise to the children that they are *calculating*, not measuring the six angles at the bottom of the sheet. Answers: **1.** 132°, **2.** 57°, **3.** 113°, **4.** 28°, **5.** 75°, **6.** 145°, **7.** 104°, **8.** 90°, **9.** 135°, **10.** 158°, **11.** 60°.

Differentiation: Some children become all fingers and thumbs when using a protractor. You can enlarge the sheet and even cut out each angle to reduce any chance of confusion, but there is no substitute for close adult supervision and help.

Extension: Let children loose with protractors to find angles (exclude right angles) on everyday objects. What are the angles on a bicycle frame? (They could sketch this and do this challenge for homework.) *Are there angles that can be measured on wallpaper patterns? Utensils in the kitchen? Sweets or other packaging?*

Know your angles (page 63)

Objective: To recognise and identify angles and to know and use associated vocabulary.

What to do: Reiterate the statements given at the top of the sheet. Children should be able to read and follow the instructions, sticking the angles into the appropriate column of the chart. They could then fix the chart into a suitable maths book or make it into a display. The sheet is marked most easily by visual reference.

Differentiation: Children who find this difficult can be given a right angle to use as a standard measure (one can be made simply by folding paper twice; alternatively provide set squares). They can compare the angle shown with the right angle. Is it less than a right angle or not?

Extension: Challenge the children to measure the angles on the sheet, accurately, using a protractor. The sheet is therefore self-marked.

Accident and Emergency graph
(page 64)

Objective: To extract and interpret data in tables and graphs.

What to do: Revise the words *mode* and *range* with

the children. Reading the graph accurately does involve making judgements as each grid line represents ten divisions so you should allow leeway for the answers. In order, from 12.01 to 21.01, the number of patients treated is 45, 54, 30, 45, 70, 88, 75, 60, 45 and 62. Answers: **1.** 574 (accept between 571 and 577), **2.** 45, **3.** 88 (accept between 87 and 89), **4.** one day (14.01), **5.** The answer to this question is not revealed by the data but it is a reasonable guess that it is the weekend. Casualties rise considerably when weekend sports matches take place, there is an increase in DIY, and GP surgeries are closed.

Differentiation: Provide close adult supervision to help children read the points on the graph. Crosses between grid lines need to be explained.

Extension: Challenge children to make a similar graph using data collected on, say, daytime temperatures in the playground. Ask them to say what the mode is.

Milkman's maths: line graph
(page 65)

Objectives: To develop an understanding of mode and range; to draw and interpret a line graph.

What to do: Although children should be familiar with graphical representations, check that they understand how to record data that does not coincide with a marked quantity on the scale, for example the need to estimate the position of 13 and 9 on this graph. The mode is 16, the range is 14. The answer to the last question is open-ended. Could it be that many elderly residents are taken out by visitors on a Sunday?

Differentiation: Less able children always seem to have the bluntest pencils in our experience – make sure they have tools fit for the job! Some children might benefit from working in pairs on this task.

Extension: Discuss with children whether it is sensible to join the points on this graph. *Are there any deliveries halfway between Tuesday and Wednesday?* Point out that points are sometimes joined on graphs in order to show trends and changes, for example the rise and fall of deliveries. The pattern of rainfall in a given month might be plotted to underline this point.

DAY	Mon	Tue	Wed	Thur	Fri	Sat	Sun
Bottles delivered	18	13	16	16	9	20	6

Taking temperatures

1. Take these temperatures.

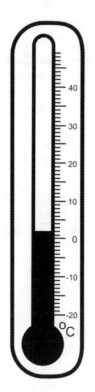 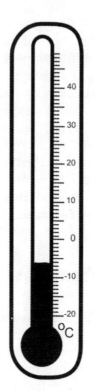   

a. _____ b. _____ c. _____ d. _____ e. _____

2. Arrange the temperatures in order, lowest first.

_____°C _____°C _____°C _____°C _____°C

3. What is the difference in temperature between the highest and lowest temperatures?

_____

4. How many degrees does the temperature fall from 2°C to –6°C?

_____

5. How much must the temperature rise by from –12°C to –6°C?

_____

6. When the temperature rises by 16° C, show what this thermometer will look like.

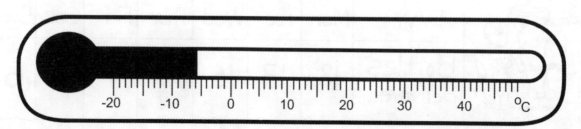

All square

● Use coloured pencils to build up squares 1 × 1, 2 × 2, 3 × 3, and so on, on this grid. Complete up to 10 × 10. Fill in the table below too.

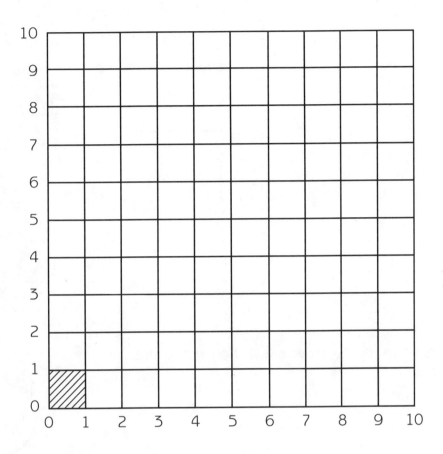

1 × 1 = 1^2 =1
2 × 2 =
3
4
5
6
7
8
9
10

● What is 9^2? _____

● What is the area of a square swimming pool 9 metres long? _____

● What is five squared? _____

● Explain in your own words what a square number is.

_____

_____

_____

_____

For every...

1. For every goal that Kafu scores, Rinaldo scores two. Kafu scored 31 goals in the season. How many did Rinaldo score?

_____

In one match Rinaldo scored 4 goals. How many did Kafu score?

_____

2. Javed eats five sweets for every two that Natasha eats. Javed eats 25 sweets. How many does Natasha eat?

_____

3. For every leg a bird has, a spider has 4. How many legs does a spider have?

_____

4. For every 5 books that Philip reads, Rosie reads 10. Rosie reads 30 books. How many did Philip read?

_____

5. Gran uses 3 apples to make ¼ litre of sauce. How many apples are needed to make 2 litres?

_____

Decimals, fractions and percentages

● Complete this chart. Then learn these facts.

fraction	decimal	%
1	1.00	
$\frac{1}{2}$		50%
		75%
$\frac{1}{4}$		
$\frac{1}{5}$		
	0.10	
$\frac{1}{100}$		

● What percentage of these shapes is shaded?

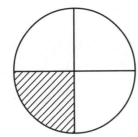

a. _____

b. _____

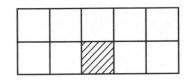

c. _____

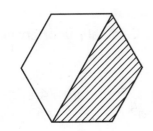

d. _____

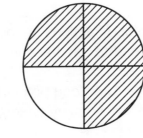

e. _____

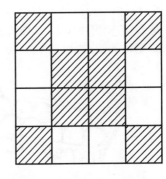

f. _____

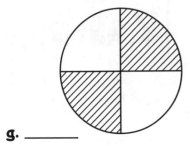

g. _____

h. _____

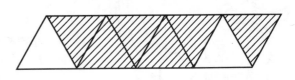

Leftovers

When you divide one number by another it does not always go exactly. What can we do about the leftovers? We can use fractions in our answers:

$$32 \div 9 = 3\frac{5}{9}$$

● Write these quotients using fractions. The first has been done for you.

a. $33 \div 8 = 4\frac{1}{8}$ **e.** $18 \div 7 =$

b. $35 \div 6 =$ **f.** $27 \div 4 =$

c. $49 \div 5 =$ **g.** $39 \div 8 =$

d. $73 \div 6 =$ **h.** $61 \div 5 =$

● Sometimes it is not sensible to use fractions in your answers. Calculate your answers to the questions below. Will you need to use fractions?

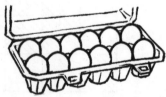

1. An egg box holds 12 eggs. There are 74 eggs. How many boxes are needed?

2. A school takes 120 children on a trip to the zoo. Each coach holds 35 children. How many coaches are needed?

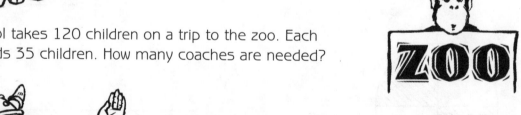

3. Opera tickets cost £48 each. How many can I buy for £250?

Estimate and calculate

Look at each calculation. Which of the three answers given do you think is correct? Circle that answer in red then use a calculator to work out the correct answer. Underline it. If your guess was correct score a point. How many points do you score out of 21?

1.	5 × 555 =	3421	2775	2510
2.	8 × 324 =	2592	4341	2012
3.	9 × 998 =	8982	8132	9832
4.	512 ÷ 8 =	50	64	36
5.	405 ÷ 9 =	68	54	45
6.	400 ÷ 16 =	20	25	31
7.	18 × 21 =	378	278	478
8.	28 × 31 =	758	998	868
9.	38 × 41 =	1738	1248	1558
10.	1296 ÷ 36 =	36	26	16
11.	576 ÷ 24 =	14	24	34
12.	289 ÷ 17 =	17	10	27
13.	72 × 55 =	3960	3510	3110
14.	44 × 71 =	2814	3124	3334
15.	85 × 34 =	890	1890	2890
16.	600 ÷ 25 =	23	24	21
17.	1024 ÷ 16 =	64	60	75
18.	1426 ÷ 23 =	62	32	82
19.	91 × 91 =	6171	8281	9111
20.	39 × 82 =	2998	3599	3198
21.	55 × 93 =	5115	6115	4995

Hot shot!

Shoot down the numbers one at a time using your calculator keys. You must shoot them in size order starting with the smallest number. Record your key presses as shown below.

key presses	display
⊖ 2 ⊜	5470
⊖ 7 0 ⊜	5400
⊖ 4 0 0 ⊜	5000
⊖ 5 0 0 0 ⊜	0

a. 7635

b. 1996

c. 4082

d. 9301

e. 3670

f. 9999

g. 10132

h. 25461

i. 43195

j. 72346

Polyominoes

Polyominoes are made from identical squares touching fully edge to edge.

There is only one monomino.

There is only one domino.

But you can make two trominoes. (If you make others you will find that they are the same as these but rotated or turned over.)

There are five tetrominoes.

● Here is one pentomino, but there are many more. Can you find them all?

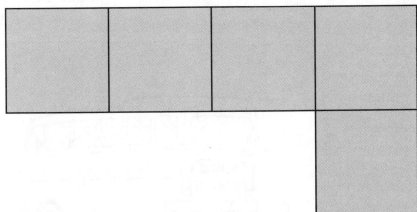

● Complete the chart:

Polyomino chart		
name	number of squares	number of possible arrangements
monomino	1	1
domino	2	
tromino		
tetromino		
pentomino		

It's a problem (1)

1. To cook the chicken the oven was set to come on at 4.45pm and to go off at 6.20pm. For how long was the chicken cooked?

_____

2. The video player started recording at 21.15 and stopped at 23.35. For how long did it record?

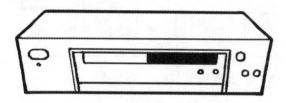

_____

3. It was 325 miles to Rye. The coach had travelled 112 miles. How much further to go?

_____

4. Mum's car does 42 miles to the gallon. She has used 9 gallons of petrol since Friday. How far has she travelled?

_____

It's a problem (2)

1. There are 21 bags of sugar in a large cardboard box. Each bag contains 2.2kg of sugar. Someone drops the box bursting 5 bags. How many kilograms of sugar are left that can be sold undamaged?

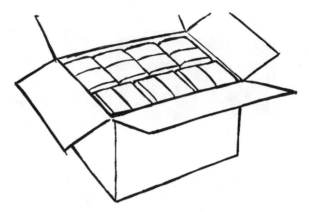

_____

2. The bank will exchange 1 Euro for every 65p. How much money will I need to exchange for 20 Euros?

_____

3. In a grand sale there is 20% off everything except lampshades and lamps which both have 50% off. How much would you save on the price of each of these items in the sale?

£1020   £86.50   £320   £24   £133   £180

a._____   b._____   c._____   d._____   e._____   f._____

4. 80 people from the village want to go to the Flower Show at the NEC. They decide to go by sharing cars. They have 20 cars between them and although they can each carry 5 people, 75% of the cars are fitted with seatbelts for 4 people only. Can they all go to the Flower Show in one journey without breaking the law?

_____

Know your measures

● Complete and remember:

A **mile** is a bit more than 1.5 kilometres and is a measure of _____.

A **gallon** is a bit less than 5 litres and is a measure of _____.

A **pint** is slightly more than 0.5 litres and is a measure of _____.

● Match the measures as shown.

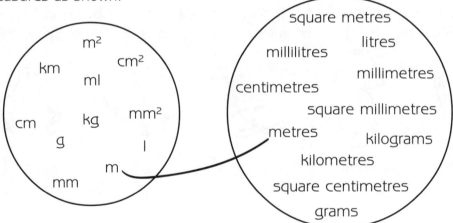

● Complete:

1. 474cm = _____ m

2. 3251cm = _____ m

3. 1400ml = _____ l

4. 5500ml = _____ l

5. 4300g = _____ kg

6. 6500g = _____ kg

Using the right measure

● Fill in suitable units of measurement.

I measured my
fish in....

I measured the length
of the classroom in...

I weighed my
fish in....

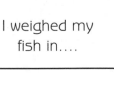

I measured the area
of the field in...

● Pour on water...

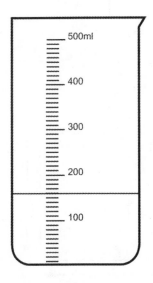

500ml

400

300

200

100

a. add 200ml

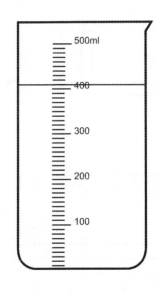

500ml

400

300

200

100

b. add 50ml

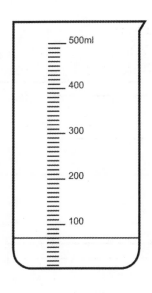

500ml

400

300

200

100

c. add 360ml

● Measure these lines to the nearest mm.

d. _____

e. _____

f. _____

Calculating areas

● These shapes are built from m². What are their areas?

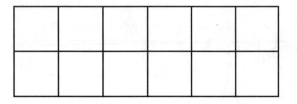

a. _____

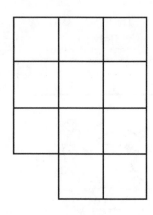

b. _____

c. _____

● Calculate the areas of these rectangles.

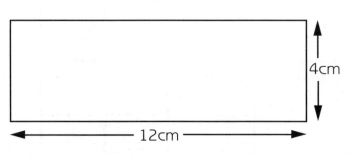

12cm

4cm

d. _____

5cm

5cm

e. _____

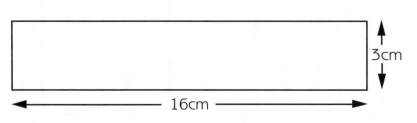

16cm

3cm

f. _____

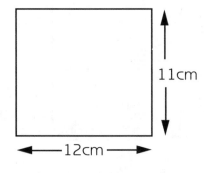

11cm

12cm

g. _____

● What is the **approximate** area of these rectangles?

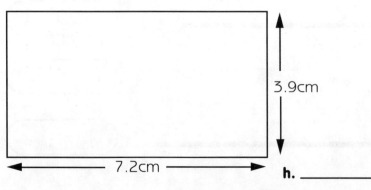

7.2cm

3.9cm

h. _____

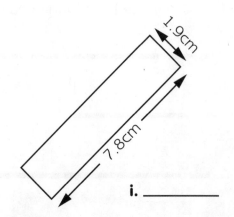

1.9cm

7.8cm

i. _____

Area and perimeter

● Calculate the area of each shape in cm² as accurately as you can.
● Measure the perimeter of each shape to the nearest mm.

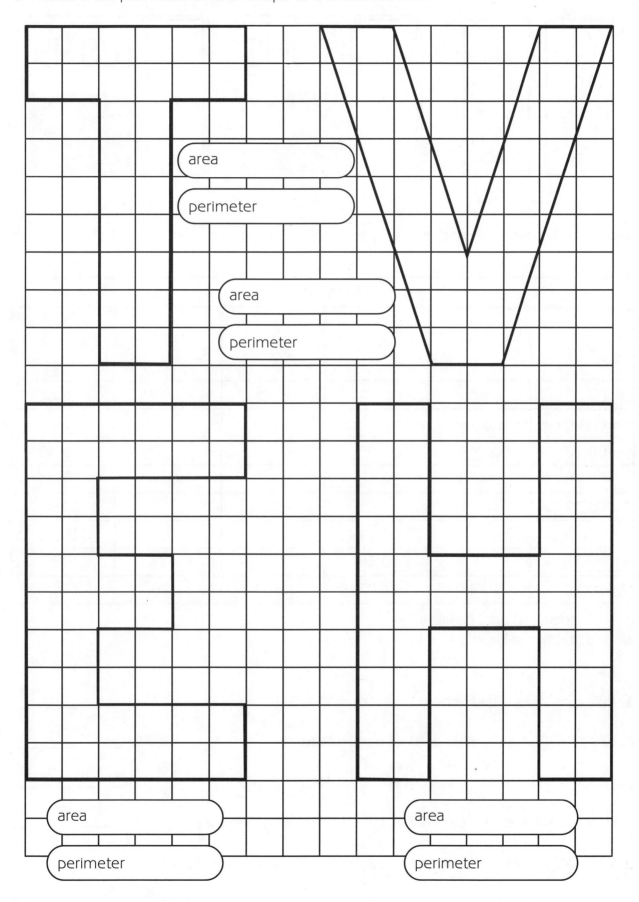

area

perimeter

area

perimeter

area

perimeter

area

perimeter

◖SCHOLASTIC   **57**

The right time

● Stick these pictures in the correct places.

● Look at this timetable and answer the questions below.

Timetable					
Oxford	Didcot Parkway	Reading	Slough	Ealing Broadway	London Paddington
05.33	05.54 c	06.12	06.20	. . .	06.40
06.40	06.58	07.20	. . .	. . .	07.39
08.22	08.44 c	09.05	09.15	. . .	09.30
08.46	09.00	09.18	. . .	. . .	09.44
08.57	. . .	. . .	. . .	. . .	09.47
09.15 sx	. . .	09.51	. . .	. . .	10.11
09.58	. . .	10.38	. . .	. . .	10.52
10.27	10.45 c	11.05	11.18	11.26	11.36

c   Change at Didcot Parkway
sx   Saturdays excepted

1. How long does it take for the 08.46 from Oxford to reach Reading? _____

2. Which is the fastest train to Slough from Oxford? _____

3. Which is the slowest train from Oxford to Paddington? _____

4. How many trains run after 09.00 from Reading on a Saturday? _____

5. Can I get a train from Oxford to Slough without changing? _____

Missing links

Link the descriptions to the shapes by drawing a connecting line where they match.

a polygon with three sides and three angles – all angles and sides are equal	
a regular six-sided polygon	
a polygon with eight equal sides and angles	
a irregular polygon with seven sides	
a polygon with four sides	
a triangle with two equal sides and two equal angles	
a triangle with all angles and sides unequal	
a five-sided irregular polygon	

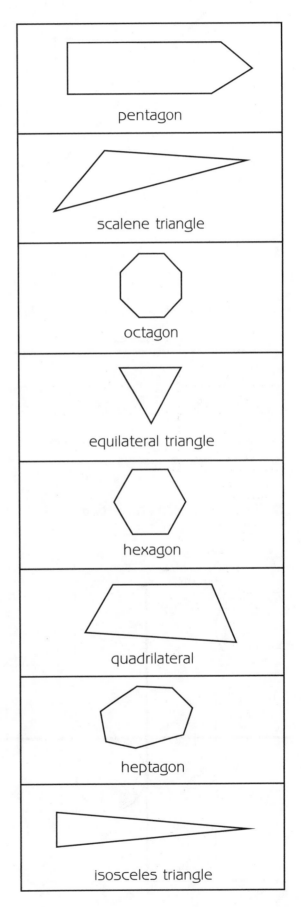

pentagon

scalene triangle

octagon

equilateral triangle

hexagon

quadrilateral

heptagon

isosceles triangle

Making reflections

● Complete these reflections in the mirror line.

1.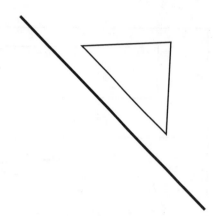

2.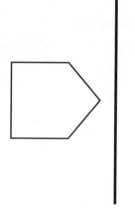

3.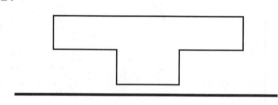

4.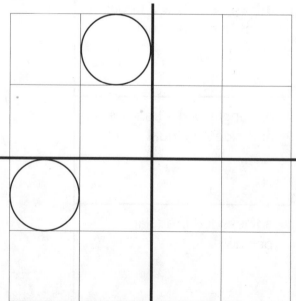

● These reflections have **two** axes of symmetry. Complete the patterns.

5.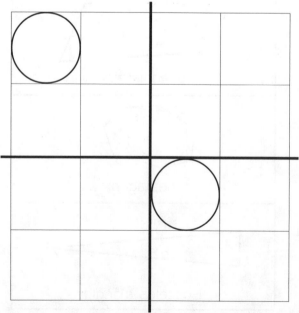

6.

Coordinated shapes

● Label the x-axis and the y-axis on the grid below.
● Mark the coordinates (1,4) (7,8) (1,8) and (7,4) in **red**.
They form the vertices of a shape. Draw the shape. What is it? _____
● Mark the coordinates (4,2) (8,10) (0,10) in **blue**.
They form the vertices of a shape. Draw the shape. What is it? _____

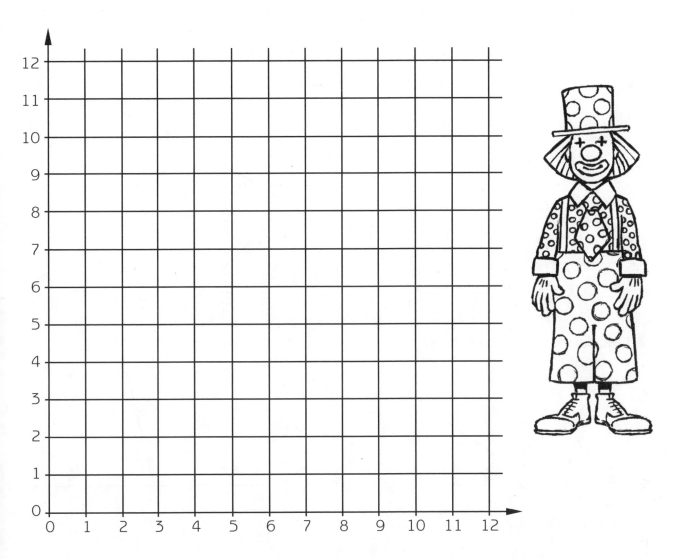

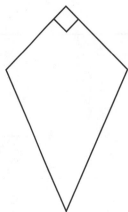

● In the shapes below, draw over the **parallel** lines in **red** and the **perpendicular** lines in **green**. Use a ruler to draw accurately.

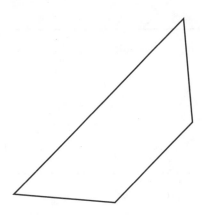
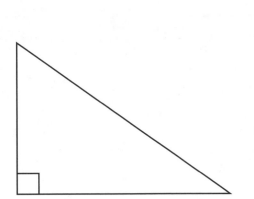

Measurement by degrees

● You will need a protractor to measure these angles.

1. _____

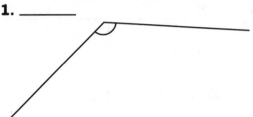

2. _____

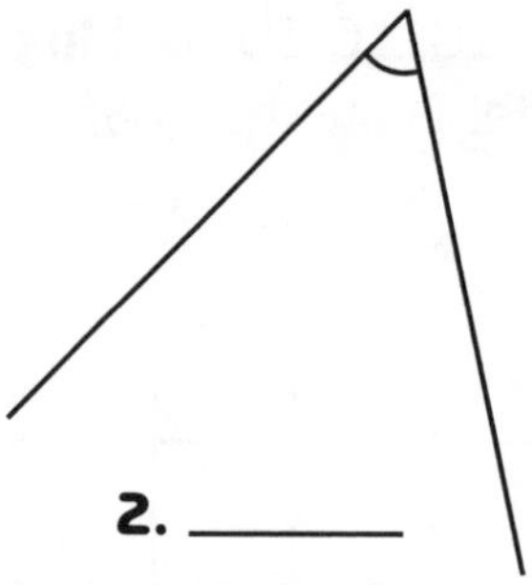

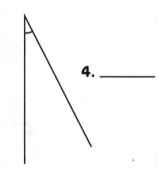

3. _____

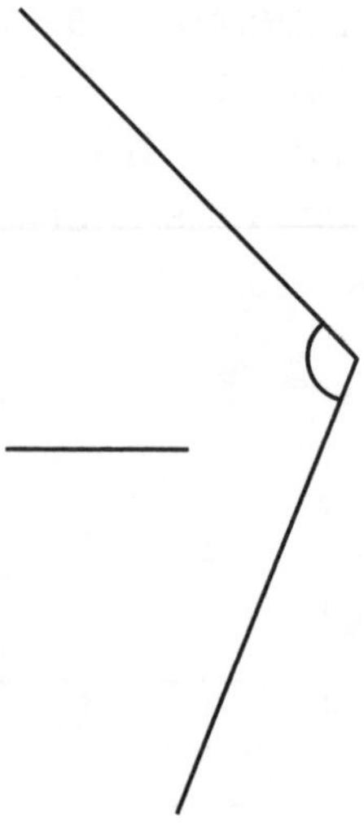

4. _____

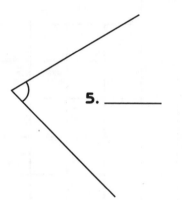

5. _____

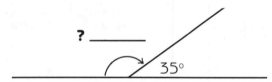

● **Calculate** the missing angles.

6.

? _____

35°

7.

? _____

76°

8.

? _____

90°

9.

? _____

45°

10.

? _____

22°

11.

? _____

120°

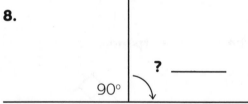

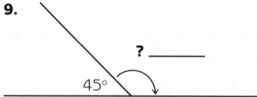

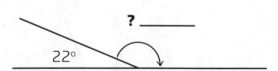

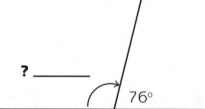

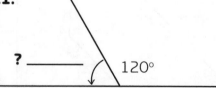

Know your angles

Learn and remember that:
- the angle of a **straight line** is 180°
- an angle between 90° and 180° is **obtuse**
- an angle less than 90° is **acute**
- an angle of 90° is a **right angle**.

Being obtuse…

Cut out these balloons and stick the angles in the correct chart.

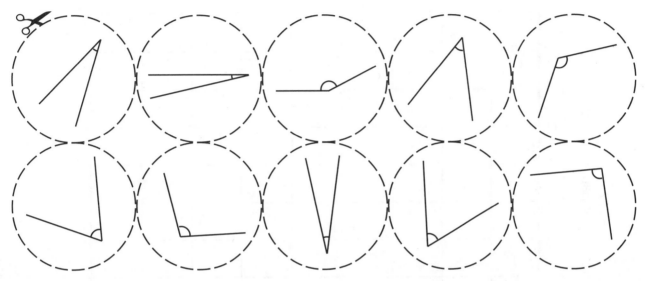

acute angles	obtuse angles

Accident and Emergency graph

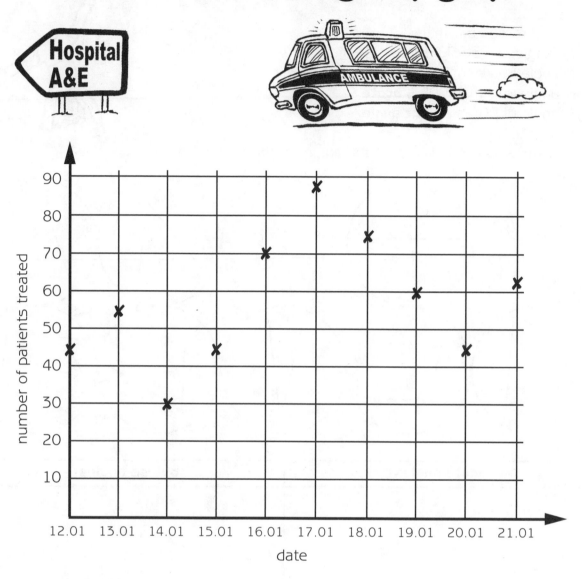

1. What is the total number of patients treated between 12.01 and 21.01 inclusive? _____

2. What was the most common number of patients treated (the mode)? _____

3. What was the greatest number of patients treated in any one day? _____

4. On how many days were fewer than 40 patients treated? _____

5. Can you think of possible reasons why nearly three times as many patients were treated on the 17.01 than on the 14.01?

_____

_____

_____

Milkman's maths: line graph

At the Meldrew Retirement Home the residents love to drink tea – lots of it. Here are the milk deliveries for one week in October.

DAY	Mon	Tue	Wed	Thur	Fri	Sat	Sun
Bottles delivered	18	13	16	16	9	20	6

● Plot the line graph of these deliveries.

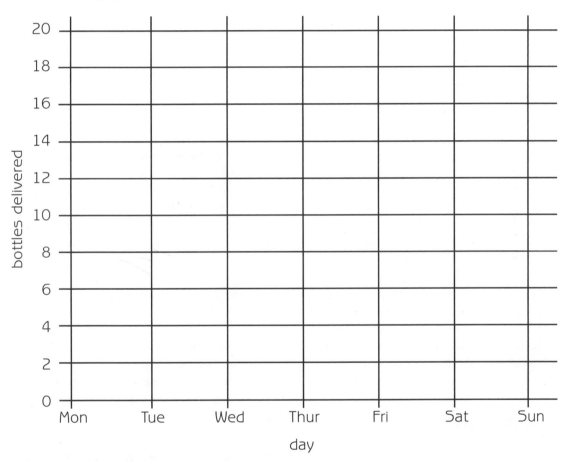

● From the data work out:

  ● the mode _____

  ● the range _____

● Can you suggest any reasons why Sunday's delivery was the smallest?

_____

_____

_____

SCIENCE

The National Curriculum science 'contexts' are 5c2 'Life processes and living things', 5c3 'Materials and their properties' and 5c4 'Physical processes'. 5c1, 'Scientific enquiry', sets out the skills and principles to be taught through these 'contexts'. To cover the National Curriculum for Year 5, the QCA scheme offers six units (5A 'Keeping healthy', 5B 'Life cycles', 5C 'Gases around us', 5D 'Changing state', 5E 'Earth, Sun and Moon', 5F 'Changing sounds') with an estimated requirement for teaching time of around 67 hours.

The modifications made to the QCA Schemes of Work when the curriculum was revised did not amount to a great deal – references to arteries and veins were removed, connections between health and diet increased and the investigation of pulse rate was modified – so the QCA scheme still forms a perfectly reliable source when it comes to content selection. We have referred to it when choosing which content to cover in our worksheets.

Many of the worksheets direct a child to 'do' rather than to work solely with pencil and paper so we strongly recommend that you check that you are properly prepared before you hand them out. We have made the assumption that the activities will be set firmly in the context of observation and experiment. Within the selected topics, the activities are limited to those objectives that worksheets are best able to support. They also follow progressively from the work covered in previous books in this series, one obvious advantage of which is that differentiated work can be accessed easily by using material prepared for other year groups.

Healthy connections (page 72)

Objective: To understand that to stay healthy we need an adequate and varied diet.

What to do: What *not* to do is to worry children about their body image or to be insensitive about family matters concerning health and diet. Obesity is a growing problem among children and a threat to health (children are not responsible for this, adults are) but this activity and the next are solely focused on the objective stated. It should not be used without adequate explanation or preparation and must be the subject of class follow-up discussion.

You will need to provide access to suitable reference material and books so that children can do the research suggested. Children can connect the

problems outlined on the sheet with the solutions by simply drawing a line. The problems were real (generally considered to have been consigned to history), although dietary deficiencies still arise in specific places and circumstances. Lack of fresh fruit and vegetables on long voyages caused scurvy and the 'trial and error' solution of giving sailors limes proved to be effective because limes contained vitamin C (hence the nickname 'Limeys'). Rickets, another disease of dietary deficiency (largely 19th and early 20th century in Britain), is prevented by foods containing vitamin D (cod-liver oil and so on). In 18th-century Paris it was found that the babies of the poor had a lower perinatal death rate than the rich. The idea that this was due to lower class babies being given potatoes and gravy that contained some vitamin C was tested and found to be correct.

Differentiation: Display lists and charts showing the various food types and information about vitamins. This will reduce the problem of research that some may find difficult. You might also reduce the scope of the sheet for less able children by setting them only one of the problems (scurvy) to research. Information on the latter will also be available in children's history books of the Tudor period.

Extension: Children should start to build up an understanding of foods that are essential to health. Ask them to collect information about healthy food from TV advertisements, supermarket displays, information on food packaging and so on. Although children do not need to understand formal classification of foods, they should understand which are essential for growth and which for energy.

Trace a torso: the heart and lungs (page 73)

Objective: To know that the heart and lungs are protected by the ribs and that the muscle in the walls of the heart contracts regularly to pump blood around the body.

What to do: Provide tracing paper, lead pencils (no harder than HB), scissors and reference books about the subject. Make sure that children can use tracing paper adequately. It may be advisable to provide ready-cut rectangles to avoid waste – children have a habit of using the middle of a large sheet! Answers: (i) The heart and lungs are protected by the ribs

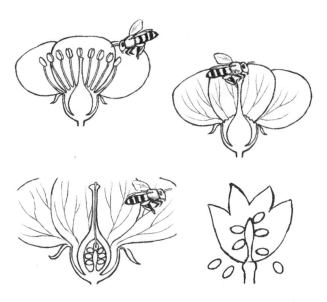

(ii) The muscle in the wall of the heart contracts to pump blood around the body.

Differentiation: Some may find the tracing exercise taxing in which case enlarge the sheet to make the work less intricate. Provide paperclips so that the tracings can be held together more easily. Make sure that the reference material is at a level appropriate to the reading ability and comprehension level of the children.

Extension: Ask the children to make simple observations about what happens to their bodies when they take strenuous exercise (breathe faster, feel hotter, become tired, sweat). Why does this happen? (Muscles have worked harder.) You may extend work further into a study of how the heart and lungs work but this is not required of Year 5 children.

Seed dispersal (page 74)

Objective: To learn that seeds can be dispersed in a variety of ways.

What to do: Revise previous learning on how flowering plants produce seeds from flowers that grow into new plants. Ideally use this sheet in the autumn. Children should not put seeds into their mouths – remember that some children are allergic to types of nuts. It would be appropriate to show examples of some of the seeds, if they are available (particularly the sycamore and ash tree seeds).

Seeds can be dispersed in more than one way but are usually designed for a specific dispersal mode. Fleshy fruits demand to be eaten (animal dispersal); non-fleshy and winged seeds will float in the air (wind dispersal) or explode and scatter widely (explosion); and some rely on water (coconuts are dispersed by the sea). There are a few difficult (that is, unfamiliar) seeds on this sheet to encourage children to make suggestions and deductions from observation and to undertake some research. Answers: Water: coconut, mangrove. Wind: dandelion, ash tree, sycamore. Explosion: some ripe cucumbers explode to hurl seeds across the ground. Animal: rose hip, blackberry.

Differentiation: The more information and hands-on experience children have, the easier this activity will be. Make sure that all the information the children require is available. Test out some dispersal methods, for example, blow dandelion seeds and test sycamore seeds by hurling them into the air.

Extension: Ask children to explain why seeds need to be dispersed (to have the best chance of growing into a new plant). Give them an extended list of fruits to classify by dispersal method, such as acorn, apple, cranesbill, tomato. (Tomato plants grow in profusion around the Kariba Dam in Africa where Italian workers helped in its construction.) This could be a task for homework.

Pollination (page 75)

Objective: To understand that plants produce flowers which have male and female organs and that insects pollinate some flowers.

What to do: This sheet should be attempted in the spring term and should be a practical activity that involves careful examination of the parts of a plant. It would be a good idea to get children to draw and label the parts of a plant (as on the sheet) from life by direct observation. All the necessary information and instructions are on the sheet. Other pollination methods are by wind, water and even human intervention (as in plant nurseries).

Differentiation: Some children will need to have the pollination process explained to them orally. You may do this with the whole class or with specific groups, according to your judgement.

Extension: This sheet can lead to a great deal of useful experimentation and scientific observation. With adult supervision you might carry out a dissection of a flower (a poppy is good). Tweezers and magnifying glasses are required. Alternatively you could carry out germination experiments. Try to get seeds to germinate under different controlled conditions (vary light, warmth, water and soil). Try cress, broad beans, lettuce, radish or spring onion seeds.

Guess the gas (page 76)

Objective: To know that air has weight and is all around us and that there are many gases of which many are important to us.

What to do: You might choose to look at the first question on the sheet as a class exercise by way of introduction. Children should name the gases used in the pictures. They may be able to do this from prior knowledge but have reference books available for children to carry out some research for themselves.

SCIENCE

What to do: It is probably best to let small groups or pairs of children do this at different times so that you can minimise resource and supervision problems. (You might choose to get children to write down their observations separately and then have a class discussion based on their observations.) The key learning is contained in the objective stated above but children should also know that gases flow more easily in all directions than liquids. Gases are more easily squashed than liquids or solids and when liquids are released from containers they run along the floor, but gases flow everywhere. NB: Closely supervise and account for any syringes used.

Differentiation: Differentiate by time allocation. Less able children will need to be given more attention and closer supervision if anything profitable is to result from the activities.

Extension: Because of safety and other practical issues it is probably best to follow up this activity by using secondary sources such as videos. Try to demonstrate the qualities of gases (they can sometimes be seen and smelled but be aware of safety issues), their dangers and usefulness. Approach your science advisor or coordinator for help.

Changing state: evaporation
(page 78)

Objective: To understand that evaporation is when a liquid turns into a gas.

What to do: Children are required to make observations and to explain phenomena in terms of scientific knowledge and understanding and as always, observation of the real thing is better than a picture. In this case all the pictures are showing phenomena that the children will have observed many times (nail polish drying and ink/correction fluid drying might be the exceptions). When the children have completed their sheets, discuss their answers. This would make a good class lesson. NB: Make sure children understand that in evaporation liquids do not disappear but change to a gas. We smell things because gases enter our noses. You should be sensitive to the fact that some solvents like nail varnish are highly flammable. Refer to guidance on solvent abuse before tackling this issue.

Differentiation: These ideas should be accessible to most children. Some might have the ideas reinforced by experiment, for example draw a chalk circle around a puddle (you can make the puddle yourself), then redraw the circle at timed intervals. *Where has the water gone?*

Extension: Ask children to describe what happens when paint dries. Watching paint dry might not be the best assignment for homework but ask children to consider what they would experience through sight, smell and touch, as paint dried.

The examples show a manned balloon (helium), fizzy drink (CO_2), gas fire (natural gas), hospital (oxygen). The latter part of the sheet is open-ended; possible answers include scuba diver, camping stove, fighter pilot and so on.

Differentiation: Information is the key to differentiated support for this activity. Make sure that information on the illustrated examples is readily accessible. Bottles of fizzy drink usually list contents on the label. Some children may not be clear about the nature of air and it would be useful to demonstrate what air does, for example fly a kite, blow up a balloon. Blow up two identical balloons, one hardly at all, the other to the maximum. Suspend them on opposite ends of a coat hanger. *Which is the heaviest? Why?*

Extension: Carry out experiments to confirm that there is 'air' in the spaces, for example pour water onto a container with dry soil in it. *What happens? Why?* Squeeze a sponge under water. *What happens? Why?* Pour water into a container with dry, loose sand in it. *What happens? Why?* (All will be revealed by the experiments! Air bubbles can be seen rising through the water demonstrating that air has been trapped between the soil/sponge/sand.)

Solids, liquids and gases (page 77)

Objective: To understand that gases are different from solids and liquids in terms of how they do not maintain their shape and volume.

Changing state: condensation
(page 79)

Objective: To understand that condensation is when a gas turns to a liquid.

What to do: Demonstrate condensation. There are a number of ways of doing this. If you use a boiling kettle as shown on the sheet, take great care, children are not the only people who can scald themselves. A container, covered in clingfilm, that contains hot water can be used to observe condensation if you place an ice cube on top of the clingfilm. All the answers to the questions stem from the fact that as water vapour cools down it returns to a liquid state.

Differentiation: The experiments are essential for those who fail to grasp the concept readily. Get out the clingfilm and ask children to observe and to record their observations.

Extension: *Where and when does condensation form in the home/car/school? Can you explain why?* Ask children to carry out a small survey of condensation sites in school or at home (for homework).

The water cycle (page 80)

Objective: To understand the water cycle in terms of the processes involved.

What to do: Use this sheet after children have studied evaporation and condensation. You might do this sheet in reverse by examining where drinking water comes from first. This can lead into an explanation of the water cycle in terms of condensation and evaporation. The labels should be cut out and stuck on the picture, although the words can be copied and written out if you wish.

Differentiation: Less confident children should cut out and manipulate the labels. Give these children help by starting them off on the cycle. As it is a cycle it does not matter where you start.

Extension: Tackle the drinking water question in more detail. Track the water back from a tap to its source. Visit the local reservoir or water works. The utility providers are usually very helpful if you plan visits well in advance. Video resources help but are not so memorable as the real thing. Children are fascinated by the recycling of water (matter is neither created nor destroyed). Question: *Is it possible we could have bathed in the urine of Julius Caesar's horse?*

Heaven's above! (page 81)

Objective: To understand some key facts about the Sun, Earth and Moon (relative size, Earth's rotation, night and day).

What to do: You will need to provide torches, globe, beach ball, pea (dried) and tiny bead (half size of the pea). Let children work in twos or threes to do the activity. Children follow the instructions on the sheet and write their answers in the spaces provided.

The beach ball is the Sun, the pea the Earth and the tiny bead the Moon. To reinforce these relative sizes you need to emphasise the distances involved. The Earth would fit into the Sun a million times over. Use the beach ball, pea and bead to recreate part of the solar system – children can hold the objects and stand the relative distances apart. The Earth rotates once every 24 hours whilst hurtling around the Sun at 68 750 mph. The Sun is 93 million miles from the Earth and the Moon is 239 000 miles from the Earth so the Sun is roughly 389 times further away from the Earth than the Moon is from the Earth. If you put the bead 30cm (try 3cm) from the pea, the beach ball would need to be 117 metres (try 11.7 metres) away from the pea to represent the relative positions of the Earth, Moon and Sun.

Differentiation: Mixed-ability grouping should satisfy any differentiation needs although it is worth stressing to children that it is hard even for adults to conceive of the vast sizes and distances involved.

Extension: Carry out an experiment to record the position of the changing position of the Sun throughout the day. Stress that the Sun doesn't move but the Earth does. Depending on the orientation of the classroom, this can be done by tracing shadows cast on the wall of the classroom by a marker on the window. A shadow stick outside is perhaps more straightforward to set up. *From which direction does the Sun rise/set?* Challenge children to calculate how long it would take to reach the Sun/Moon riding their bikes at 10mph (or Concorde at 1500mph).

The Moon's orbit (page 82)

Objective: To know that the Moon takes approximately 28 days to orbit the Earth and that the different appearances of the Moon provide evidence for the 28-day cycle.

What to do: Children need to be able to read and understand the text. They should only attempt this after appropriate preparatory observations (such as the previous sheet). NB: The actual period of the Moon's revolution around the Earth is 27.3 days but because of the Earth's progress around the Sun, the Sun's light strikes it at a slightly different angle by the end of the month so that we see the phase repeat every 29.5 days.

Differentiation: Children who are unable to cope with the level of literary comprehension demanded by this sheet will need to be taught in a small group and carry out the activity by being given oral instructions.

Extension: Ask children to tell the story of man's first journey to the moon. They should find out the dates, the names and the facts and prepare a report for the

class. This could be a suitable homework task. Challenge children to find out why we only ever see one side of the Moon from the Earth.

Vibrations (page 83)

Objective: To understand that sounds are produced when objects vibrate.

What to do: The groundwork for this sheet should include some introduction to sound that demonstrates that it is caused by vibrations. Show children a vibrating tuning fork, a plucked elastic band, dried peas bouncing on a banged drum, and ask them to feel a struck cymbal. Carrying out the activity on the sheet should not then be difficult.

Differentiation: You can provide help with the language by asking groups of children to brainstorm appropriate words to go with the pictures. Write the useful words on cards and let the children use them as a wordbank when they do the activity.

Extension: Investigate sound travel. Can children find out how fast it moves? When they hear a car in the street outside the classroom what has the sound travelled through to reach them? (Air, brick, glass and so on.) Which is better at travelling through things – light or sound?

Metronome muffling (page 84)

Objective: To understand that some materials are more effective than others in preventing sound sources from reaching the ear.

What to do: Set out the equipment and materials required. Small groups of children should do this work at different times. This is not suitable for whole-class work – unless you have many metronomes and sound-proofed cubicles. Discuss the issue of 'fair testing' before the experiment begins. *How can you be fair about judging the loudness of the sound heard?*

Differentiation: Differentiation is likely to be by the amount of time and support provided. Mixed-ability groups are probably best for this task.

Extension: Ask children to investigate where, why and how we need to muffle sound effectively (road noise, machinery noise). This is a possible homework task.

Changing pitch: wind instruments (page 85)

Objectives: To understand that sounds can be made by air vibrating and to understand how the pitch of the sound can be altered; to test this knowledge practically.

What to do: You might demonstrate how a wind instrument works by blowing across the mouth of a bottle. Ask children to suggest how the sound is made. *What is vibrating?* Put water in the bottle and ask

children to predict what will happen to the sound. This class activity can be followed by the activity on the sheet. To make the panpipes you will need to provide thin plastic hosing (12mm to 16mm across) or similar, sticky tape and card and Plasticine or other material to bung up the ends of the tubes. The playing method is: purse lips, smile and blow – easy with practice. Children should predict what will happen first, that is before testing their prediction by blowing.

Differentiation: Some will be unfamiliar with the instruments illustrated. Play recordings of them (*The Young Person's Guide to the Orchestra* by Benjamin Britten is ideal). You may be able to have a musician perform on some of the instruments. Instead of making the pipes some children could simply test their ideas by blowing across an assortment of plastic tubes or cases. Take care! Small tubes can be swallowed and block air passages. If in doubt, don't.

Extension: Challenge children to vary the length of a tube to produce a note close to one played on an instrument (chime bar, piano or recorder). Test the challenge for yourself first so that you can suggest a suitable note for them to tune to. Remember, you cannot add to the tube once it is cut.

Changing pitch: stringed instruments (page 86)

Objectives: To understand that the pitch of a stringed instrument depends upon the length, thickness and tightness of the string; to test this knowledge practically.

What to do: Carry out the tests as described on the sheet. This is obviously something that requires at least two children. You may be able to provide more than two thicknesses of string, but try not to complicate matters too much – there are already three variables. The violins are drawn in size order, which is also pitch order (left to right: violin, viola, cello and double bass).

Differentiation: Although this can be arranged so that two, or with variation, one child alone can do it, less able children should work in threes – one to hold the string, one to sit and one to pluck. Supervise well so that children stay on task. Making noises is fun but they need to make observations and deductions too.

Extension: Can children make the sound louder? Ask them to tie a piece of string all the way round an empty wooden drawer (from handle back to handle). Pluck the string over the open drawer. *What has happened to the sound made by the string?* Challenge children to 'tune' the string (by varying the tension).

Banging on (page 87)

Objective: To understand that the pitch of a drum depends upon its size and the tightness of its skin.

What to do: Provide children with a range of drums and allow them to experiment with playing them at suitable times (and places!) before giving them this sheet to work on. In order to carry out the experiment they will need one tuneable drum and beaters. Make sure that the children understand that the instrument is delicate and expensive and, like all school property, should be treated with respect. The pitch of the drums illustrated falls broadly in order of size: kettle drum, tenor drum, side drum, tom-toms.

Differentiation: Make this a group activity for those who require support, although some tuneable drums can require adult strength to operate properly so adult supervision and help may be required.

Extension: Make a class collection of pictures showing different drums and drummers. Make sure it is a multicultural collection. This could be useful research for homework. Challenge children to put the drums in likely pitch order using the knowledge that they have gained about drums.

Healthy connections

The food we eat every day is called our **diet**. **Health** and **diet** are connected but people did not always know this.

● Use books to find out about food and vitamins then see if you can make the right connections below.

What was the problem?

What did they do about it?

Scurvy
Sailors on long voyages became ill with scurvy due to a lack of vitamin C.

Fed them potatoes, lemon juice and milk.

Rickets
Young children developed soft bones that became bent due to a lack of vitamin D.

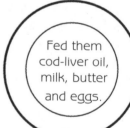

Fed them cod-liver oil, milk, butter and eggs.

The death of babies
In Paris, babies from rich families had a diet containing less vitamin C than the babies from poor families so more rich babies died.

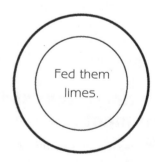

Fed them limes.

Brain teaser
● Why did the Americans give the British the nickname 'Limeys'?

_____

_____

Trace a torso: the heart and lungs

● Trace each rectangle and the drawings they contain onto tracing paper. Cut the rectangles out. Put the body together correctly by placing the sheets on top of each other.

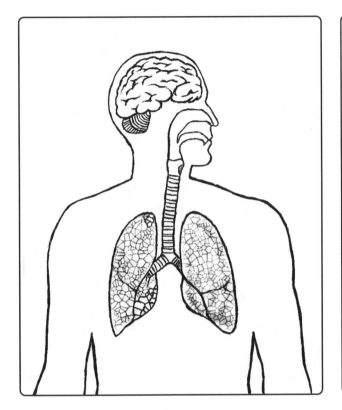

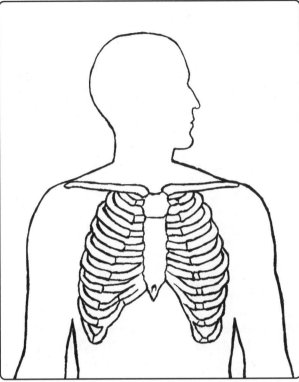

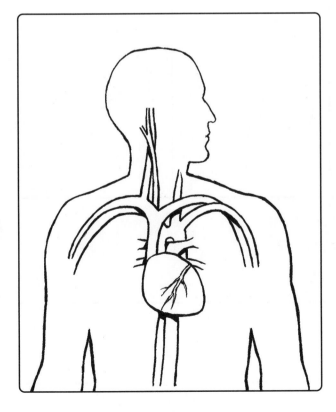

● Find out:

● What protects the heart and lungs?

_____

● Why does the muscle in the wall of the heart contract regularly?

_____

● Add to the drawings. Label the brain, lungs and any organ you can name to which the heart pumps blood.

Seed dispersal

● Seeds can be dispersed in a variety of ways. How are these seeds dispersed? Put them in the correct column in the table below.

| dandelion | rose hip | coconut | sycamore |
| mangrove | cucumber | ash tree | blackberry |

water	wind	explosion	animal

● Why might some seeds not grow into new plants?

_____

● Why do plants produce so many seeds?

_____

Pollination

Most flowers have **male** and **female** parts. The **stamens** are a flower's male parts and produce **pollen**. The **stigma** and the **ovary** are the female parts. Pollen settles on the stigma and **fertilises** the seeds. Seeds will not grow unless they have been fertilised.

● Study the pictures and read the text. Colour pollen yellow and show its journey from picture to picture.

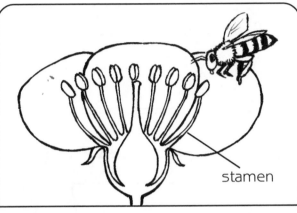

1. When collecting nectar an insect brushes against the stamens and pollen sticks to its legs and body.

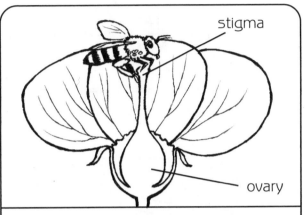

2. When the insect visits another flower, pollen brushes from its body against the stigma.

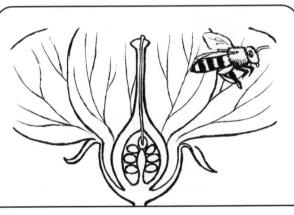

3. The pollen passes down the stigma to the ovum where it fertilises the seeds.

4. When the seeds are ripe they disperse. If they land on moist, light ground, a new plant will grow.

● Not all flowers are pollinated by insects, pollen can also be carried by animals such as birds and bats. Find two other ways in which flowers can be pollinated.

_____

_____

Guess the gas

● Air has weight and is all around us, but you can't see it. How do you know that it exists?
● There are many gases. Can you name the gases used in the pictures below?

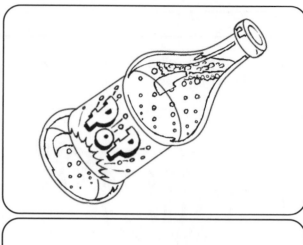

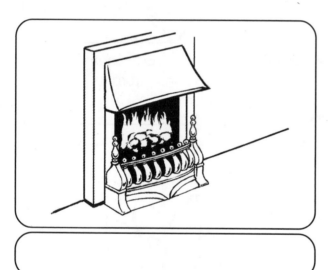

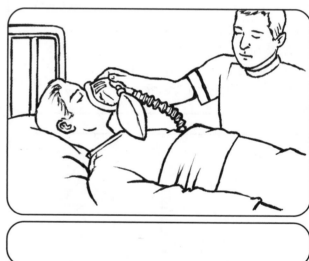

● Draw two other examples showing where gases are important to us.

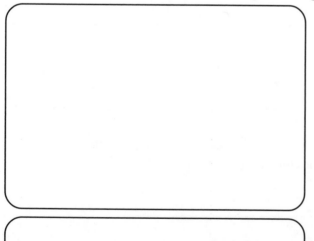

Solids, liquids and gases

● Do the activities drawn below with a friend. Talk about what is happening.

Pour water from
bottle to glass.

Push in a syringe filled with
air, then water, then sand.

Fill a balloon with
air, then water.

Transfer flour from
container to bowl.

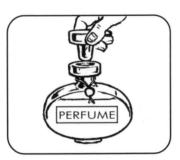

Release the stopper
on a bottle of perfume.

Take the lid off a
fizzy drink bottle.

● Think about the differences between solids, liquids and gases and then write down as many differences as you can think of on the chart below.

solids	liquids	gases
have a definite shape	take on the shape of their containers	

Changing state: evaporation

● What happens to puddles when it stops raining?

● What happens to wet washing when it is hung on the washing line?

_____

_____

● What happens to...?

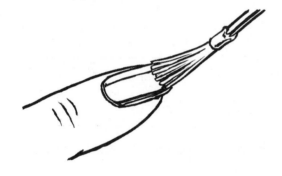

● What happens to...?

_____

_____

Evaporation is when a liquid turns to gas.

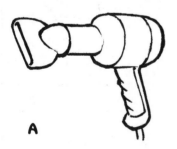

A

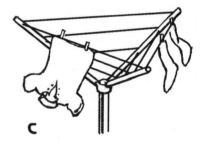

B

C

● Explain how these (**A**, **B** and **C**) help to dry things more quickly.

A _____

B _____

C _____

Changing state: condensation

Condensation is when a gas turns to a liquid. It is the **reverse** of evaporation.

● What happens to water vapour when it cools down?

_____

_____

● On which surfaces will water condense in these rooms? Mark them.

● Complete the sentence:

Air contains w_____ v_____. When this hits a c _____ surface,

it forms c _____.

● Why is there less condensation on windows on a warm day?

_____

The water cycle

● Cut out the labels and stick them in the correct places on the picture to show what happens in the water cycle.

water condenses	water evaporates	sea	rain	river	moving air/wind

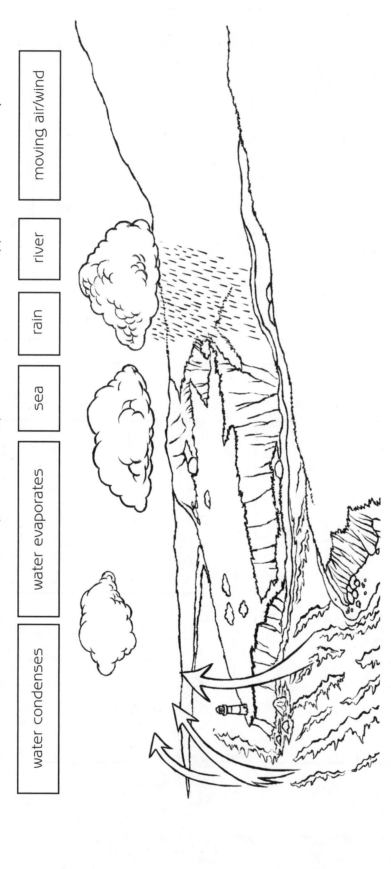

● Fill in the gaps:

Water _____ from oceans and lakes. It _____ as clouds and eventually falls as _____.

Water collects in streams and _____ and eventually finds its way back to the _____.

● Where does your drinking water comes from?

Heaven's above!

● The Sun, Moon and Earth are approximately spherical. Think about how big they are. Which of these spheres would you choose to represent each heavenly body?

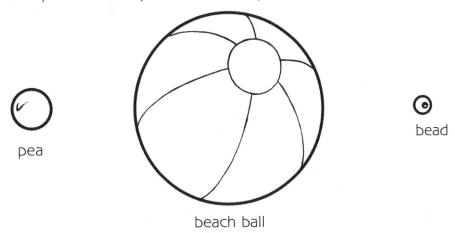

pea

beach ball

bead

_____   _____   _____

The Sun does not move.

The Earth spins on its axis.

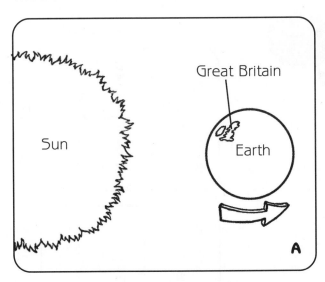

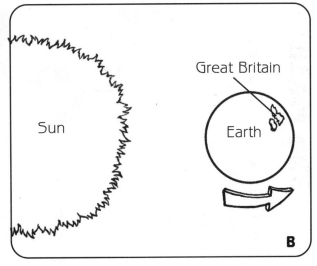

● With a friend, use a torch (to represent the Sun) and a globe in a dark corner of a room to help you decide in which picture **A** or **B** (above) you would be asleep in bed. Explain your answer.

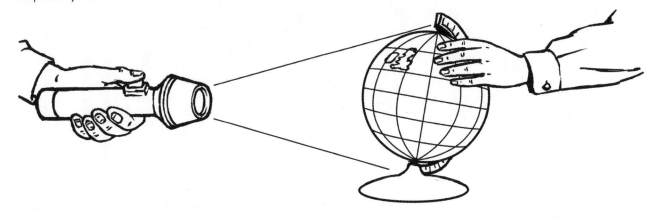

The Moon's orbit

The Moon appears to change shape because of the way the Sun shines on it as it circles the Earth. The Moon orbits the Earth roughly once a month.

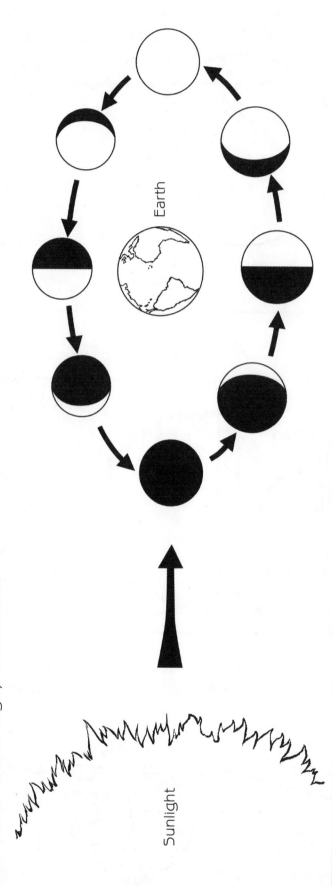

Earth

Sunlight

Half of the moon is lit up when it is a quarter of the way round its orbit.

It is a **new Moon** when the Moon is between us and the Sun.

As the Moon moves around the Earth, some sunlight catches the edge of the Moon and we see a **crescent Moon**.

When the Moon is exactly opposite the Sun, all the sunlight falls on its surface and it is a **full Moon**.

More and more of the Moon is lit up as it orbits the Earth. It reaches its **gibbous** stage when a crescent appears to have been cut out of it.

The changes are reversed as the Moon continues to orbit the Earth – from **gibbous** to **half Moon** to **crescent Moon** and finally, to **new Moon** again.

Draw an arrow from each label to the correct phase of the Moon.

Vibrations

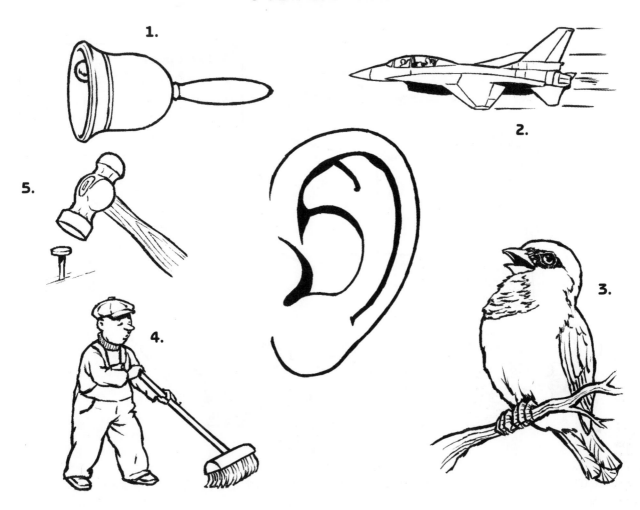

What sound is being made in each picture? Describe it. Is it high-pitched or low-pitched? How do you think that the sound is being made? What is vibrating?

1. _____

_____

2. _____

_____

3. _____

_____

4. _____

_____

5. _____

_____

Metronome muffling

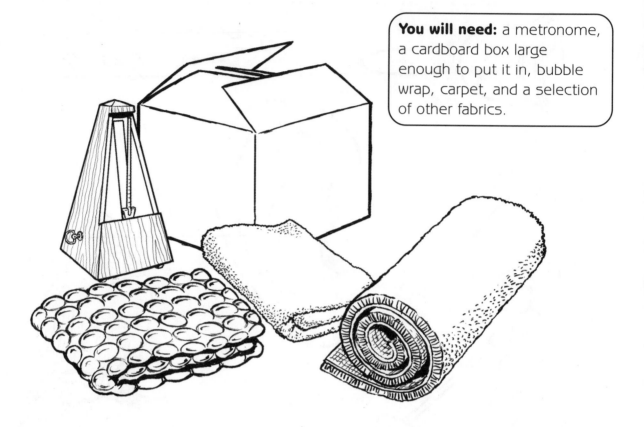

> **You will need:** a metronome, a cardboard box large enough to put it in, bubble wrap, carpet, and a selection of other fabrics.

● Set the metronome and put it in the empty box. Shut the lid. What happens to the sound?

Experiment

● Use different materials to line the box and make a fair test to see which are best at muffling the sound. Record your results for each material. Predict what might happen first.

Material	Prediction	What actually happens

Changing pitch: wind instruments

Pitch is how high or low a sound is.

In wind instruments, the pitch changes according to the length of the column of air that is vibrated. The bigger the column, the lower the pitch.

● Place these instruments in order, according to pitch, starting with the lowest-pitched instrument.

Answer: _____

_____

Pan pipes – make and test
● Play the pipes by blowing across the top of each tube. Which tubes make the highest notes? Can you explain why?

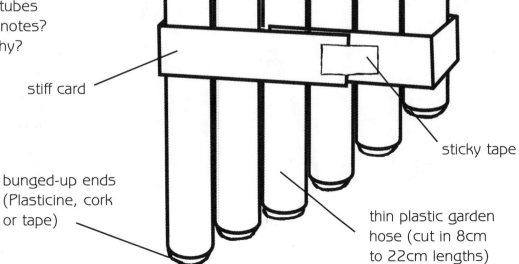

stiff card

sticky tape

bunged-up ends (Plasticine, cork or tape)

thin plastic garden hose (cut in 8cm to 22cm lengths)

Changing pitch: stringed instruments

● Tie a piece of string (80cm) to a chair leg. Pull it tight. Twang it. Try this several times using a different length, thickness and tightness of string. Describe what happens to the pitch of the notes that you make.

_____

_____

_____

_____

_____

The violin family
● Match the labels to the correct instrument.

(cello)   (violin)   (viola)   (double bass)

● Which has the lowest pitch. Why?

_____

Banging on

● What do you think will affect the pitch of a drum? Write your prediction here.

_____

_____

_____

● Now bang a drum!

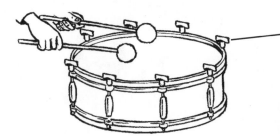

Use a drum whose skin can be tightened by turning these screws.

● Finish the sentences:

When I tightened the screws, I found that _____

_____

_____

When I loosened the screws, I found that _____

_____

_____

● Put these drums in order of pitch, starting with the lowest-pitched drum.

side drum (or snare drum)

tom-tom

kettle drum

tenor drum

HISTORY

The history National Curriculum for Key Stage 2 is open to considerable variation. The six units – a local history study, three British history studies ('Romans, Anglo-Saxons and Vikings in Britain', 'Britain and the wider world in Tudor times', and 'Victorian Britain' or 'Britain since 1930'), a European history study (Ancient Greece) and a world history study – do not even need to be taught separately. In practice the number of curriculum variations adopted by schools has tended to be quite small, the most common pathway through the historical maze being the broadly chronological one, with Ancient Egypt the most popular world history study. This is the path that we have followed here, although clearly we could not include sheets to service all possible local history projects.

In selecting our activities, we have focused on National Curriculum topics and the periods selected by QCA for Years 5 and 6 in their Scheme of Work for history, although that still left plenty of scope for choice. The periods covered in this chapter are Victorian and post-war Britain since 1948. Because of the way in which the National Curriculum is set up, teachers may choose to do the history in a completely different order. Obviously we could not allow for all possible variations but we have tried not to make the worksheets too age-specific. Moreover, if you choose to study topics other than the ones we have chosen, we would refer you to other books in this series where your choice has very likely been addressed. You might wish to note that the QCA allocate (depending on choices) between 30 and 42 hours to history in Year 5, although you can choose to do more.

It is not by accident that each of the history units in the QCA Scheme of Work is headed by a question. Interrogating evidence to find out about the past is a major part of what children should be doing whatever history they are studying in the primary school and asking questions is the key. The 'headline' question is, of course, only a beginning and it should raise other questions in the children's minds. It is, in fact, an excellent strategy to ask children to think of questions that they themselves would like answering as this provides extra motivation for their research. *Did Victorian children go to school? What games did they play? What clothes did they wear?* and so on.

Although there is a little background historical information in these notes, you are advised to refer to other reference material for more detail. There are plenty of books available. For succinct overviews of the historical topics in the National Curriculum at Key Stage 2, see: *History* in Scholastic's *Pocket Guides to the Primary Curriculum* series.

© INGRAM PUBLISHING

Images of a queen: Victoria (page 91)

Objective: To identify Queen Victoria, facts about her life and the period in which she lived.

What to do: Most Year 5s will be able to cope with this sheet although it is worth reading through the text and dealing with any difficult words, for example *population*. The idea is that children should make a decent illustrated presentation of facts about Queen Victoria. Ask them to mount the rearranged text and pictures on coloured paper. Alternatively, scan into a computer and direct children to do this as an ICT activity.

Differentiation: Deal with textual difficulties by asking children to underline every word that they are not sure of and then making sure that these are explained before any cutting out begins.

Extension: You could do a direct comparison with Queen Elizabeth II. Ask children to search for three comparable images (stamp, mug, recent photo). They could write a similar potted history of this queen's reign (a possible homework task). There is plenty of scope to explore further the changes within the Victorian period. Look at changes in the home, in war, in dress, in buildings, in domestic life, in medicine, in science, in transport and so on. It is a long and revolutionary period so there is plenty of change to choose from. The Victorian sheets in this chapter can form part of this study.

Victorian people who made history (1) (page 92)

Objectives: To collect information from a range of sources and to find out about important figures in Victorian times; to understand that the work of individuals can change aspects of society.

What to do: Let children treat this as a detective exercise. They should work in small groups of, say, three, and start by studying the picture clues. Do they know anything about this person? From there they should move on to look in books or on CD-ROMs for more information. One child could be elected 'scribe' to whom the others must report back *orally* what they have found so that he or she can record it succinctly (on a separate piece of paper).

Differentiation: Group support should be sufficient to enable less able children to get the most out of this task but you could make sure that more simplified texts are set aside for their particular use. Make sure that the dictionaries of biography and reference books deal with the people named.

Extension: You may wish children to present their findings in more extensive ways. Groups of children could carry out detailed work for one particular biography – share the people around the groups. In class discussion, raise the issue of the impact individuals can have on history. *What difference would it have made if Turner or Nightingale had never lived?*

Victorian people who made history (2) (page 93)

Objectives: To collect information from a range of sources and to find out about important figures in Victorian times; to understand that the work of individuals can change aspects of society.

What to do: Treat this sheet in the same way as the last. All the figures should be well known to adults.

Poor children at work (page 94)

Objective: To understand a number of aspects of daily life for poor Victorian children.

What to do: The commissioners quoted extensively from interviews that they conducted with children and others and although these quotations were not always verbatim (we too have changed some text into the first person), the facts and sentiments were unaltered. Let children work in groups. Ask them to list all the facts given in the evidence before they start to compare their day with that of these children.

Differentiation: Less confident readers might simply be allocated the design task or be asked to give a verbal account of the differences between their day and that of factory children.

Extension: Ask children to consider how to solve this 'exploitation' problem. *Why did parents allow it to happen? What do they think should be done? What did the Victorians do about it?* (Laws about children working in mines and factories; laws insisting that children went to school.)

© M PLEDGE

Timeline of change: Victorian schools (page 95)

Objective: To use a timeline to recap main events, dates and figures to help recall some of the main changes in the lives of children during the Victorian period.

What to do: Instruct the children to cut out each fact and arrange them in date order. There are enough clues for this to be fairly straightforward. If children have a timeline (perhaps a class one), the facts could be slotted into their correct places on the line among other Victorian facts. The suggestions and questions at the end of the sheet are pointing children in the direction of useful follow-up. Direct children to study a real Victorian building – they may indeed be at school in one.

Differentiation: The terminology may confuse some children. Talk through the difficult phrases. *What is an* Act? *What do we mean by* state *as in 'state-aided'?* History becomes more and more a literary subject as children progress up the school so therefore help with language is often the most needed form of differentiation.

Extension: Children may have visited a Victorian school or enacted a Victorian school day as infants but it is worth revisiting the experience at this higher level. See if there is a 're-enactment' site close by and arrange a visit, for example The Ironbridge Gorge Museums in Telford (01952 432166 or visit www.ironbridge.org.uk), Leeds Industrial Museum, Armley Mills (0113 263 7861), Katesgrove Schoolroom, Reading (0118 901 5490) and so on (there are many). Slates and slate pencils can be bought in museums of childhood such as the ones in Edinburgh and Bethnal Green, specialist toyshops and in some French supermarkets! An excellent reference book for re-enacting a day is *The Victorian Schoolday*, a Teacher's Manual, by W Frankum and J Lawrie, available from Katesgrove Schoolroom, Reading RG1 2NL.

Decade decisions (page 96)

Objectives: To place pictures in the correct decade on a post-war timeline; to recognise some differences between now and then.

What to do: This is a 1950s timeline sandwich. The bias towards the 1950s is deliberate. Let children select a different colour for each decade. All 1960s pictures could be linked to the decade by a blue line, the 1950s by a red and so on. The pictures shown are: 1950s: Teddyboy, the Queen's coronation, ration book, Morris Minor, Bush TV; 1960s: *Music to twist to* record, Mods on Lambrettas. 1940: Anderson shelter, gas mask.

Differentiation: Plenty of reference material must be available to support those who need it. Working cooperatively helps.

Extension: Arrange for a visitor of an appropriate age to come to talk about growing up in the 1950s. Let the children interrogate the person. Prepare the questions to be asked beforehand to keep the visit focused. Let the class brainstorm questions and help with sifting out the wheat from the chaff. Ask them to fetch one 1950s photograph or object from home to use in a class display.

Changing faces: immigration (page 97)

Objective: To communicate understanding of changes that have happened to the British way of life since 1948.

What to do: Children used to interrogating evidence will manage this activity without trouble (you won't need to deal with statements such as *they all have two legs*). Children will come up with a variety of answers of lesser or greater significance and none should be dismissed. Ask why they noticed that point particularly. Perhaps the four most significant facts are: **1.** They are all West Indians. **2.** They are nearly all men. **3.** They are all wearing suits. **4.** Some are wearing hats. *Why should this be?* (Men came first to seek jobs and probably came dressed in 'Sunday best'.) The empathy activity is difficult and its success will depend on how much knowledge children have of the reality of the experience. Talk about what it is like to be a stranger, a new child in a class perhaps. *What differences would a Jamaican have noticed from his homeland?* (One government official remarked that they would all go home when they had sampled the weather.)

Differentiation: This activity will mainly be differentiated by outcome although you may give some children the support of working with a partner on the first part of this activity.

Extension: The ethnic variety now apparent on the streets of Britain would not have been so in the early

1950s. Some children may pick up on the fact that settlement in Brixton was started by accident. *Where else did large concentrations of immigrants settle?* Discuss why this should be. (Many immigrants went to where previous immigrants had settled.) *Is this a good thing today?* Look at ethnic mix in your school. *How would this compare with the 1950s or Victorian times?* You might check old admission registers held in county record offices.

1950s money (page 98)

Objective: To look in detail at one change in an aspect of life in Britain since 1948.

What to do: This sheet can be used 'cold' but a class lesson illustrated by a display of pre-decimal money would be an excellent precursor. The answer to the bill total question is 3 pints = 1/6d, 10lbs potatoes = 10d, 12 eggs = 4/–, 2lbs of flour = 1/–, Total cost = 7/4d (seven shillings and four pence, approximately 37p). The problem is that of place value and caused problems to children (and to foreign visitors) in those days. Pence change into shillings when there are 12 (base 12), shillings change into pounds when there are 20 (base 20) – and all in the same sum. Today we work solely in base 10. Point out to the children how lucky they are!

Differentiation: Some will struggle with the arithmetic. Work with these children in a group. Set out a board (as per the sum) and use counters to represent the coins. Add up and change as you go from the pence to the shillings column.

Extension: Ask children to see if they can track down a 1950s coin at home. *How much is it worth today?* (The answer is nothing – they are not legal tender – but you can convert to decimal money and also check on the coin market via a coin catalogue.) Ask children to add up the same bill of milk, potatoes, eggs and flour using prices from a modern supermarket. *How much would the same goods cost today? What has happened?*

Images of a queen: Victoria

● Here are three pictures of Queen Victoria. Which pieces of text do they go with? Cut out the pictures and text and arrange them in chronological order (where you can) to make an illustrated article about the Victorian age.

Queen Victoria reigned for almost 64 years. This is longer than any other British monarch. She died in 1901 aged 81.

Victoria married Prince Albert and had nine children. When Albert died in 1861 at the age of 42, she went into mourning and never fully recovered. She withdrew from public life for many years. She left all Albert's rooms just as they were when he died.

When she was only 18 years old in 1837, Victoria's uncle, King William IV, died. She became Queen.

During Victoria's long reign Britain changed enormously. When she came to the throne, railway building had just begun but by 1870 there were 13 562 miles of track across the country. The Victorian age was an age of great inventors, scientists, writers and artists.

The postal service (known as the 'penny post') was invented in 1840 and telephone services began in 1890. The population grew so quickly that the Victorians struggled to cope with enormous health and housing problems. London had under 3 million inhabitants when the Victorian age began but was up to 6.5 million at the time of Victoria's death. The Victorians were great builders. They built more houses, more public buildings, more hospitals, schools and churches than anyone before them.

Find out more

● Choose two subjects from this list and write a few sentences about them.

royal palaces	royal events
Sandringham	Coronation
Balmoral	death of Prince Albert
Osbourne House	jubilee

© INGRAM PUBLISHING

Victorian people who made history (1)

When did these people live? What made them famous? Write a few sentences about them. The pictures will give you some clues but you will need to do further research.

William Gladstone

Emily Brontë

Florence Nightingale

Earl of Cardigan

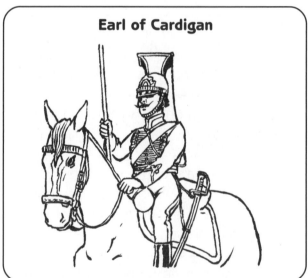

Joseph Turner

Charles Dickens

Victorian people who made history (2)

Find out when these people were born and when they died. What made them famous?
Use information books and other sources to write a paragraph about each one.

Isambard Kingdom Brunel

William Booth

David Livingstone

Charles Darwin

Dr Barnardo

Annie Besant

Poor children at work

● Study this picture of a Victorian child working as a trapper. Trappers were young children who opened doors for coal trucks down in the mines.

● Not everybody was poor in Victorian times, but for those who were, life was very tough – especially if you were a child. Poor children usually went to work in mines, mills and factories. Reasonable people were appalled when they learned how hard life was for children so the government sent inspectors to report on working conditions. People demanded that something be done about it. Read what the inspectors found out.

<table>
<tr><td>

Boy aged 12

"I worked 12 hours a day down the pit and got 6d ($2\frac{1}{2}$ p) a day. I was so tired I fell asleep once and got thrashed."

</td><td>

A young child

"I don't like being in the pit. I work in the dark as a trapper."

</td></tr>
<tr><td>

Girl aged 13

"I work from 6 in the morning until 7 at night. I have an hour for dinner but my mother is very poor so I have no tea. My father was killed in the pit. Sometimes I have enough to eat, sometimes not."

</td><td>

Girl aged 12

"I know my letters but I can't spell my name. I earn a shilling (5p) a week which my mother keeps. I work from 6.30 in the morning until a quarter to nine at night."

</td></tr>
</table>

● Compare a typical day in your life with that of a poor Victorian child.
● Imagine you lived in Victorian times. Design a poster or write a newspaper article to campaign against what was happening to Victorian children.

Timeline of change: Victorian schools

During Queen Victoria's reign the government decided that it must see that ordinary children had the chance to receive an education. These children would grow into adults who would be able to vote one day, so they must be educated! The children of the rich had always been educated privately.

● Some of the changes in schooling are listed below. Cut them out and put them on a timeline showing the order in which they happened.

Education in state schools was made free in 1891.

1846 – a teacher training scheme was begun.

In 1839 the government appointed Her Majesty's Inspectors to report on the quality of state-aided schools.

An Education Act was passed by Parliament in 1870 to allow Board Schools to be set up using public funds. They charged pupils a fee.

Education for children up to ten years old became compulsory by law in 1880.

In 1833 Parliament granted £20 000 to help the work of Church Schools that were educating the poor. This was the beginning of state education.

By the time of Queen Victoria's death in 1901, over 90 per cent of children aged five to 11 were enrolled in schools.

● Is there a Victorian school like this near where you live? Look for signs and clues. Does it have a bell tower? Separate entrances for boys and girls? Draw some sketches.

© M PLEDGE

Decade decisions

Study these pictures. They belong to the three decades shown, but which one? Connect them to the correct decade.

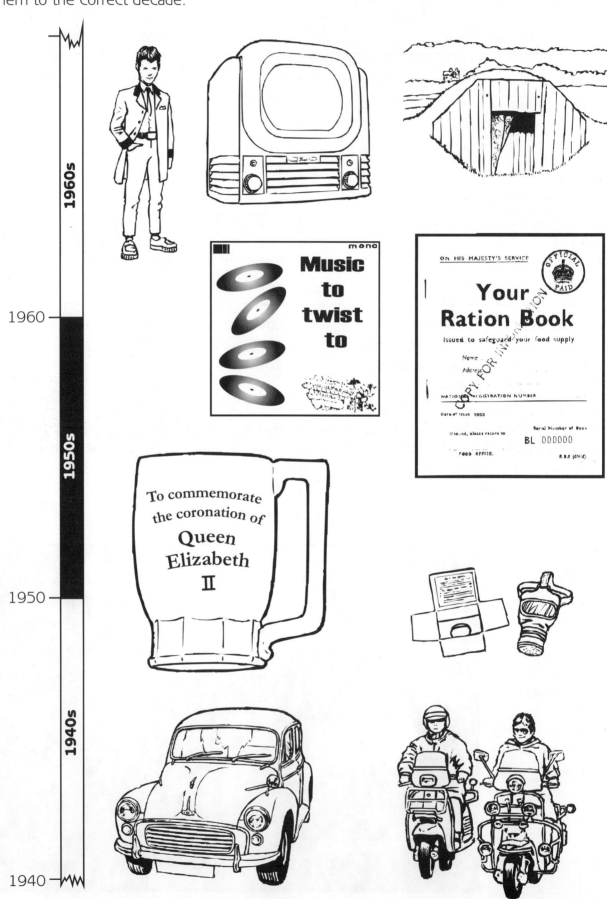

Changing faces: immigration

● Look carefully at this photograph. Write down four significant things that you notice about the people in it.

TOPFOTO.CO.UK

1. _____

2. _____

3. _____

4. _____

On 22 June 1948, the ship *Empire Windrush* docked at Tilbury on the Thames estuary. It was carrying 492 passengers and 18 stowaways from Jamaica. As they all had British passports, they were entitled to come to Britain. The government gave many of them accommodation in a wartime deep shelter on Clapham Common that was used as an emergency hostel. The nearest Labour Exchange (a place to seek work) was Coldharbour Lane, Brixton.

● Imagine that you had just arrived on the *Windrush*. Write down your first impressions of Britain.

● Imagine that you were a British child living in Brixton at the time. Describe your first meeting with the newcomers.

1950s money

This is how money worked in the 1950s:

£1 was £1 just like today but it was made up of:

    240 pence (1 penny was written 1d)

    12d equalled one shilling (written 1/–)

    30d equalled a half-crown or 2 shillings and 6d (written 2/6)

● Confused? Try this shopping bill. Can you work out the total cost?

SID'S STORES
HIGH STREET, NEWTOWN

£.s.d.

3 pints of milk
at 6d a pint

10lbs of potatoes
at 1d per lb

12 eggs
at 4d each

2lbs of flour
at 6d per lb

	pounds £	shillings s	pence d
milk			
potatoes			
eggs			
flour			
total			

● How many shillings made £1?

GEOGRAPHY

Children's progressive geographical development, in the four areas defined by the National Curriculum ('Geographical enquiry and skills', 'Knowledge and understanding of places', 'Knowledge and understanding of patterns and processes', 'Knowledge and understanding of environmental change and sustainable development') takes place through the topics set down in the 'breadth of study' section of the National Curriculum's Programme of Study.

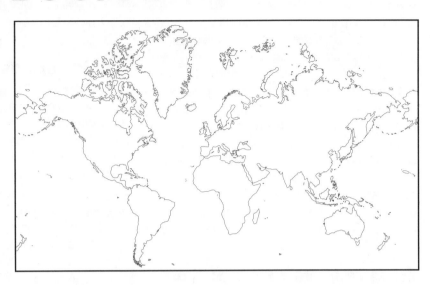

For Year 5, the QCA's geography Scheme of Work (which is, of course optional, but a useful guideline) suggests a basic three units of study to cover this with an estimated time allocation of between 32 and 51 hours – once again, an increase on the previous year. There is also an overarching unit to be dipped into throughout the key stage ('What's in the news?') and two additional units (24 to 40 hrs) that were added when the scheme was revised. You might find it useful to refer to the QCA matrix of curriculum coverage (Revised appendix 4, pages 16–17 *Geography Teacher's Guide Update*) and the websites at www.nc.uk.net or www.dfee.gov.uk/schemes.

For the activities on the sheets in this section we have focused on topics that the QCA refer to as 'long' in that they are more likely to provide substantial work over a period of time. We have covered Unit 11 'Water' and Unit 23 'Investigating coasts'. We have steered clear of the local topics and the contrasting locality (Llandudno might not be much of a contrast if you live in Llandudno) as they should clearly be teacher-directed. Curriculum content in this year group has strong links with PSHE and citizenship, not only through the local traffic study or the news topic, but through looking at erosion, the impact of humans on the environment and through understanding the importance of water, its ownership and cost implications. (For links see QCA *Geography Teacher's Guide Update*, page 11.)

Wet and dry map (page 102)

Objective: To obtain information from maps and atlases about wet and dry areas of the world.

What to do: Using an atlas is not that straightforward, especially as this activity demands the skill to seek out particular data. You may feel that it is necessary to review how to handle one. Look at the different types of map, how to use the index, explain how a map key works and so on. This task also presupposes that you have atlases available of sufficient quality and detail for the task set. Check that your atlases are up to the task. Children could use CD-ROMs and the Internet to access information about deserts. Although children might complete this sheet individually, it is suggested that a plenary discussion be held at the end. What deserts have they discovered? Which is the largest? Which is the driest place in the world? The wettest? (*The Guinness Book of Records* is a useful source.)

Differentiation: You can cut down research difficulties by carefully selecting the resources that you give to children. Some children can be pointed in the right direction, others will need to be led by the hand. Enlarging the sheet will make the activity easier.

Extension: Investigate how people cope in areas of low and high rainfall. You could study the work of aid agencies in areas of drought. Organisations such as Christian Aid provide information about the problems some people in underdeveloped countries have obtaining their daily supplies of water. Children can compare this with their own ease of provision.

What use is water? (page 103)

Objective: To understand how water is used.

What to do: This activity is about collecting and organising data. The first part of the sheet should be undertaken by pairs or small groups of children. Make sure that children spend time reflecting on the uses of water. A few glib answers are not enough. Have they thought of water fountains, swimming pools, street cleaning, watering the bowling green? Recording a week's water usage at home is meant to be about the *variety* of uses but you might also get children to estimate quantities. Discuss how they might do this.

Alternatively, this could be an in-school activity where the class study the variety of water uses in the school.

Differentiation: Make sure that you support less able children by placing them in groups of mixed ability. The activity can be made more challenging for more able children by removing the examples given under each heading.

Extension: Compare and contrast water uses in different homes. If you feel it necessary to be particularly delicate in this matter, you could provide children with your own water diary and let them compare their water diary with yours. Issues of wastage and water conservation can also be dealt with at this point. *What do we do in times of drought?* (Hosepipe bans, bricks in the cistern, no car washing.) *Should we take these sorts of measures all of the time?*

From reservoir to tap; from dirty to clean (page 104)

Objective: To carry out an experiment to observe how water is cleaned.

What to do: This topic could usefully start with a visit to a water treatment works. Discuss, as a class, the process illustrated on the sheet. You could cut out the stages illustrated and ask children to rearrange them in the correct order. Children should be left to experiment with the water cleansing (ideally a paired activity). You can assess the success of the activity if the finished product is placed in transparent containers and clarity compared. Please take particular note about not drinking the water (smell it instead). Explain the reasons to the children and make sure that you supervise closely those children likely to be tempted.

Differentiation: Some children will need help with the experiment. Small mixed-ability groups are once again a good strategy but an adult may need to start them on the first stage of cleansing. Remind children that the process will take some time, for example to let the larger deposits settle. You should have other tasks for children to do while they wait for this process to be completed. (They could describe in their own words what happens in a water-cleansing plant.)

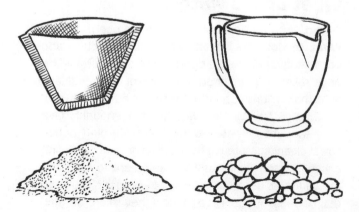

Extension: There are history and PSHE links to this topic. Ask children to find out about waterborne diseases. *What happened in the past when there were no water-cleansing plants?*

Water costs money (page 105)

Objective: To understand about water bills and the problems associated with the notion of owning water.

What to do: Children can tackle this sheet cold, but if they do so you should certainly have a class session afterwards. Many children will find the notion of paying for water new to them and most will never have seen a bill like this. Examine it. There are good links here with citizenship. Look at how the bill is set out. Discuss what each part means.

Differentiation: This may pose reading difficulties so some groups may require adult input. Don't be too eager to intervene, even less able children can work out meanings given time.

Extension: Ask children to investigate water supply in their home (for homework). *Where does the water enter the house? Where is the stopcock? The water meter? The water tank? Can you calculate the average cost of water per day at home?* (You can use the example on the sheet as an alternative for this exercise. Use a calculator.)

Coastal zones (page 106)

Objectives: To identify coastal features using maps and atlases; to use appropriate geographical terminology.

What to do: Provide good quality resources. Children do not need to look at the whole of Britain and you may choose to provide detailed maps of a coastline area close to you. Geological maps should be available but you will need to discuss with children what they show and how they show it. You may like to provide examples of soft and hard rock for children to examine. Children can tell them apart quite easily. For example, rub two pieces of chalk or limestone together and examine the dust. Rub two pieces of granite together. Note the difference. Although the answers need to be open-ended (there are many), this exercise will have more relevance if you can focus on an area of coastline that the children are familiar with. This topic would fit readily into a planned field-study trip to a coastal area.

Differentiation: This is not an easy activity. Getting to grips with tongue-twisting terminology is a challenge in itself (*depositional landforms*). Much will depend on how much introductory work you can do. Try to show videos or use CD-ROMs that show the features under examination. Less able children may need to work in an adult directed group.

Extension: Ask children to bring in seaside postcards

of Britain illustrating features discussed on the sheet, for example Flamborough Head, Pegwell Bay. Make a class display of the pictures. You can link them with a large wall map so that children can locate the places shown.

© COREL

Erosion (page 107)

Objective: To identify erosion landforms from photographs and to understand the impact that human activity may have on coastal environments.

What to do: The answers to the photographic questions are **1.** arch, **2.** stack, **3.** cave. Human activity answers might include building, road construction, walking, climbing, mineral extraction, fossil hunting and other such activities. We have focused on a particular erosion incident (Holbeck Hotel Scarborough, June 1993) because, by using the Internet and other sources, children can track down data and pictures to use in their report, but you may choose another incident if it is more appropriate. This is a chance for children to use their ICT skills and produce a report with illustrations using a word processor.

Differentiation: Provide good quality maps and atlases of the British Isles. You can narrow down the areas of search for those children whose knowledge of the British Isles is inadequate. Once again, most children will find this exercise easier if it is done cooperatively.

Extension: Have a class debate about the Holbeck incident (or similar). Imagine that you have prior warning of the event. What do children think should be done about it? Conservation action? Abandonment? Compensation? Blame? Encourage children to think about the issues raised.

The beach (page 108)

Objectives: To know about the different types of beaches, to identify them using keys on an Ordnance Survey map and to begin to understand the impact that humans may have on coastal environments.

What to do: The symbols used for sand and shingle can be found in the key to all OS maps. Provide the children with coloured pencils to draw the symbols. It is worth checking that children can find the information and definitions required from the resources that you provide them with. (Check that groyne, for example is included.)

Differentiation: Pictures of the features referred to would be a bonus and particularly helpful to less able children. Good quality source books on geography should be readily accessible in the classroom.

Extension: *Why should we want to keep a beach intact?*

Should nature be allowed to have its way? Have a class debate about the issue. You may have access to an environmentalist who could talk to the children about the issue. Look at how the sea has changed our coastline in recent history. (Sandwich used to be a busy port, the Roman fort at Richborough in Kent used to be on the coast.) You might look at major disasters like the East Coast floods of the 1950s.

We do like to be beside the seaside (page 109)

Objective: To use maps and secondary sources to research and to describe an area of coast suitable for a particular type of holiday.

What to do: The instructions on the sheet can be followed fairly easily although you may wish to have a talk about the types of holiday illustrated and the children's preferences. The last activity is a fairly substantial one. Make sure that children understand what is required. Show them a holiday brochure. Explain the meaning of the word *itinerary*. It is for you to decide on how much time you allocate to this, but children could produce a substantial piece of art and design or ICT work. Alternatively you can keep this small scale and let children design their brochure on the back of the sheet.

Differentiation: Children may work on this in pairs or even in small groups as if they were producing a small magazine. Less able children will benefit from group work but you may need to intervene to direct them from time to time. *Is it worth including maps, pictures, timetables, instructions?*

Extension: Let each group make a holiday presentation to the class about their destination. Ask children to write an illustrated list of rules for tourists who wish to protect and conserve the coastal environment, for example stick to footpaths, take photographs not specimens and flowers, leave the car at home and so on. Alternatively design a poster or advertising jingle.

Wet and dry map

Use an atlas and any other useful reference book, to complete a wet and dry map of the world.

● Colour blue the parts of the world with very high rainfall.
● Colour red the parts of the world with very low rainfall.
● Label the main deserts of the world on your map.

What use is water?

● Make a list of the uses of water and sort them under these headings.

 Home	 Farm	 Industry	 Leisure	Other
				?
washing up	growing crops	cooling	water skiing	firefighting

● Keep a record of the ways in which water is used in your home.

Monday	Tuesday	Wednesday	Thursday	Friday	Saturday	Sunday

From reservoir to tap; from dirty to clean

Water must be thoroughly cleaned before it is fit for us to use.

● First, water is collected in reservoirs where any solid material can settle to the bottom.

● Then water is pumped from the top of the reservoir into the treatment plant.

● In the treatment plant the water is flowed through filter beds of sand and gravel to remove any debris and smaller impurities. Chlorine is used to kill any germs that might be left in the water.

● The clean water is pumped into the water supply pipes and then travels to our homes.

Investigation

● Can you clean water? Take a small quantity of dirty pond water and clean it using the materials shown here. (Remember what you have just read.)

Remember!

When you have finished, do not drink your clean water. It may be cleaner than when you started but there will still be some invisible germs.

Water costs money

● Study this water bill. Who supplies the water in this area? _____

● Who owns the water? _____

● What is the charge for water supply (before VAT)? _____

● Why is there a charge for used water? What does it mean? _____

_____

Severn Trent Water

Date (and tax point) 1 June 2000 Vat Reg No. 486 9555 65	Invoice No 959000035

Account enquiries call (at local rate)

0845 6033 222

Your account number

You can call us 8.00am to 5.00pm Monday to Friday

Dear Customer

This is your Water Services Invoice for the period 4 May to 30 May 2000.

The amount due is
£9.26

The amount shown is payable within 7 days.

We are required to charge VAT on bills for customers whose Standard Industrial classification (SIC) Code falls within categories 1-5. The SIC Code held on our records is 48300 (Group 4). If this is incorrect please advise us in writing.

M = This is an actual reading

Water Services Invoice

Balance brought forward					£0.00
Sub Total					£0.00

Service	Meter No 97032	Latest reading	Previous reading	Volume (cubic metres)	Pence per cubic metre
Measured water supply		5(M)	0	5.00	77.08
Measured sewage				5.00	47.74
Measured Drainage - Comm Band 01					

Charges				VAT	Charge
Water Standing Charge				17.5	£1.17
Water Supply				17.5	£3.85
Used Water Standing Charge				Zero	£0.58
Used Water				Zero	£2.38
Surface Water Drainage Band 01				Zero	£0.40
Total charges for this period					£8.38

VAT @ 17.5%	£5.02	£0.88
VAT @ 0%	£3.36	£0.00
Total VAT		£0.88
Total charges including VAT		£9.26

Amount Due	**£9.26**

● Who supplies the water to your home? _____

● How much does your water cost? _____

● Do you have a water meter in your house? _____

● How does your bill compare with this one? _____

_____

● Rain is free. Nobody owns it. Why should we pay for water? Write down some reasons.

Coastal zones

The zone where the land and sea meet is called the c _____ .
The sea can wear away cliffs and rocks.

Erosion landform

The sea can also build up the coast by deposits.

Depositional landform

● Study a map of a coastal area of Britain. (Use a geological map if you can.) Look for **headlands** formed where the sea cannot wear away **hard rock**. Look for **bays and beaches** where **soft rock** has been worn away by the sea.

● Using a map, make lists of places in Britain that are:

Headlands	Bays	Erosion landforms	Depositional landforms

Erosion

● Look at these photographs. Which erosion landforms do they show? Are they caves, arches or stacks?

> **Caves, arches** and **stacks** are examples of **erosion landforms** caused by the action of the sea.

1._____

2._____

3._____

● Human activity can also cause coastal erosion. Can you think of any ways in which we do this?

● In June 1993, the Holbeck Hotel in Scarborough collapsed into the sea (see right). Find out how this happened. Write an illustrated report about it.

The beach

The sea can carry sand and shingle and deposit it on the coast to form a beach. Beaches are the most common **depositional landform**.

● Look at the symbols on a large scale Ordnance Survey map and find out what symbols are used to show:

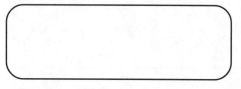

sand beaches   shingle beaches

● What are the main differences between a sandy beach and a shingle beach? Describe them in your own words.

_____

_____

● Beaches sometimes have to be managed to keep them intact. Use a dictionary or encyclopedia to find out what the following are. Explain and illustrate the terms.

cliff-face armouring	groynes

artificial harbours	sea walls

We do like to be beside the seaside

● Choose from the following the type of holiday you would most like to have.

● Use maps, books, the Internet and travel brochures to make a short **list** of suitable locations for the seaside holiday.

_____

_____

_____

_____

_____

● Choose one of these places and make a **brochure** about the place. Produce a holiday **itinerary**. Work out how you will travel and how long it will take to get there.

DESIGN AND TECHNOLOGY

Design and technology in the National Curriculum is concerned with *developing ideas, planning, making products*, and *evaluating them*. This can be done by (1) investigating familiar products, (2) practical tasks (for developing skills and techniques) and (3) designing and making products. It is suggested, in the QCA Scheme of Work for design and technology, that between 31 and 39 hours be spent on the subject in Year 5. Although these estimates relate solely to the scheme, they do provide a yardstick against which to measure curriculum time allocation. Two of the original QCA units for Year 5 underwent changes following revision of the National Curriculum but the four topics in the scheme remain: musical instruments (5A), bread (5B), moving toys (5C) and biscuits (5D). The sheets in this section can be used to service elements of these topics.

Practical experience is the key to all learning in design and technology so work must involve a great deal of 'designing and making'. This element has therefore been included in our activities, which means that using these sheets generally involves the need for materials and equipment as well as close supervision and appropriate health and safety precautions.

Structures (1): striking sounds
(page 113)

Objectives: To understand the principles by which different instruments work; to produce a quality instrument that will produce a series of controllable sounds when played (percussion) by joining and combining materials and components accurately.

What to do: The foundation work on which this sheet builds is the investigation – taking apart and working out how they function – of a range of musical instruments. This experience should precede working on this sheet. From this knowledge the children can go on to develop a clear plan for making an instrument of their own. In order to carry out the activity children will need the materials listed (at least). The experimentation element is essential but the final product need not resemble any on the sheet. You may provide alternative, but similar, materials and you

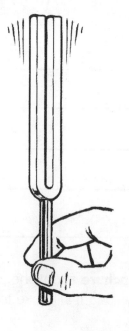

should encourage children to be inventive.

Differentiation: Direct less able children to replicate one of the instruments illustrated if they are devoid of ideas of their own. Give them plenty of time.

Extension: Although the focus of this sheet is on activity, you might require children to 'write up' their work, describing what they did and the results of their experimentation with the instrument. They might include their answers to the questions asked on the sheet. This could be a task for homework.

Structures (2): tunes from tubes (page 114)

Objectives: To understand the principle by which different instruments work; to produce a quality wind instrument that will play a series of controllable sounds by joining and combining materials and components accurately.

What to do: This activity is built upon the same premise as the last but you may need to revise how a sound is produced by a wind instrument. The blowing technique could be demonstrated by a child musician or other wind player. This is a sheet that contains a lot of direction and may be more suitable for less skilled or less imaginative children, but you should encourage children to use their initiative when designing the instrument. NB: As these instruments are to be put into mouths, you should be aware of health and safety risks. Don't encourage children to share instruments and remember to sterilise tubes with mild antiseptic.

Differentiation: This is obviously an activity-based sheet and you will need to give the less dextrous children plenty of time to complete it. Differentiate by time allocation and by the degree of adult help offered. If necessary, you may wish to provide ready-made funnels for some children.

Extension: Ask children to think about controlling the sounds that they produce. Can they make more than one note? A skilled wind player could demonstrate what can be done with expertise and lung power. Tunes have been played on cisterns, taps and even snorkel tubes! Get children to collect names and pictures of as many wind instruments as they can. This could be a homework task.

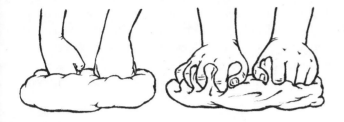

Using your loaf (1) (page 115)

Objectives: To understand that there are a wide variety of breads and bread products; to work safely and hygienically, weighing and measuring accurately, to produce bread.

What to do: Talk about bread and 'bread products' with the whole class. Illustrate the importance of these foods to our diet. (Make sure you include fruit loaves, Chelsea buns, croissants, and so on.) Point out the bread variations in different parts of the world and in different traditions. Making bread should be something the children will do in small, supervised groups. They should all eventually make the basic bread. NB: You will need to carefully manage the class groups as considerable supervision will be necessary. Address the issue of health (*Is bread good for us?*) and hygiene. Be scrupulous about cleanliness when cooking.

Differentiation: Differentiation will be by degree of supervision and the less able children should work in the smallest groups.

Extension: There are many avenues to explore. Health is one possibility – the key idea is that we should eat plenty of bread. *Which sort of bread is best for us? Should we add plenty of butter and jam?* You could organise a survey of the quantity (by weight) of bread products consumed by children over a period of time and present the results graphically. Compile a book of sayings, quotations and poems that refer to bread: 'Use your loaf', 'Patter cake, patter cake, baker's man', 'Man cannot live by bread alone' and so on. A visit to a large supermarket or bakery to list the breads on sale is worth undertaking. You might examine the ingredients listed on packaged bread, for example Mediterranean Ciabatta contains: wheat flour, water, black olives (3%) with acidity regulator lactic acid,

tomato paste (3%), sun-dried tomato (3%), extra virgin olive oil (1.5%), basil, salt, yeast and malt flour. *What are all these ingredients? What is their function in the mixture?*

Using your loaf (2) (page 116)

Objectives: To understand that there is a wide variety of breads and bread products; to work safely and hygienically, adapting a basic recipe.

What to do: This is part of the bread investigation initiated in the last sheet. The idea is that, having made the basic bread recipe, children go on to try variations for themselves as part of a 'design and make' assignment. Different groups could make the variations suggested so that a range of products are manufactured. This is a small-group activity for which a classroom assistant is an almost essential requirement. It is not a sheet simply to be handed out and 'done' unsupervised or without proper preparation. You will need to decide which ingredients you are going to provide. You may request children bring their own to meet their particular requirements or the variations that they wish to try out. Health issues will arise during this project. It may be worth keeping parents informed as there may be children with nut allergies or similar. You may wish to note that QCA offer a very similar alternative project based on biscuits rather than bread – you should do either one or the other, not both.

Differentiation: Once again differentiation will be by degree of adult intervention and supervision, although less able children should work in the smallest groups.

Extension: Children could write up their project as if it were a scientific experiment and they should at some point evaluate the success of their work. Did they achieve what they set out to achieve? You could organise a classroom *Ready Steady Cook* with the children challenged to explain what they have done in a few words and to give their new product a name. Collect bread recipes and compile a class 'Bread Book'. Challenge children to find a recipe for a particular bread for homework. Supervised use of the Internet at home could be included. Consider cultural variations and traditions associated with bread. Have a demonstration of cooking by a foreign cook – French croissants, Italian ciabatta, Indian chapattis and so on. Regional variations in the British Isles are also worth exploring. Produce a bread map of Europe or the world.

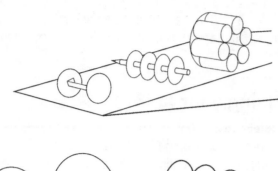

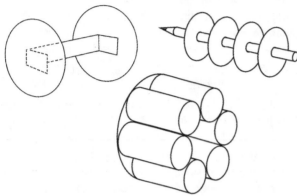

Mechanisms (1): moving along

(page 117)

Objective: To recognise a cam within a mechanism and how it changes movement; to understand that a cam changes rotary motion into linear motion.

What to do: This, and the next activity, focuses on how movement can be controlled using a cam in a simple mechanism or toy. Ideally preliminary investigations should involve examining a collection of toys that use cams. The best of these are the simple type made for very young children (for example, where a figure moves up and down in a car seat) although on many toys the cam is encased. Consult your D&T coordinator about this. The school may start its own resource collection.

It will be a matter of judgement as to what materials and tools you provide for the children to use and you should include instruction in how to use tools such as files and drills in your D&T lesson. The sheets merely point children in the direction of worthwhile investigative assignments. You will need to give children time and not too much instruction. We have tried not to show 'the answers' in the form of finished products on the sheets but it has been hard to avoid. Let children add the finishing touches (the toys could be decorated and embellished in all sorts of ways and the mechanisms could take many forms).

NB: The use of glue guns is not proscribed but like many apparently 'harmless' items of equipment can cause injury if not used under proper supervision. Use files and glue guns only after instruction and under strict supervision. D&T, like most of life is not, however, risk free.

Differentiation: Some children may benefit from working cooperatively on this, although you might challenge a more able child to complete the task alone. Essentially teachers should keep a low profile once the activity is underway. Let children make mistakes and try a number of solutions. Adults should only intervene when frustration begins to set in with a vengeance. Children will learn by trial and success.

Extension: Challenge the children to describe how their 'invention' works, using an extensively annotated diagram.

Mechanisms (2): moving around

(page 118)

Objectives: To recognise a cam within a mechanism and how it changes movement; to understand that a cam changes rotary motion into linear motion; to understand that different shaped cams produce different movement.

What to do: See 'Mechanisms (1): moving along', above. This time, clearly, we are focusing on different movement being produced by different cams, hence 'rollarounds'. Explaining 'out loud' is an excellent way to test understanding. If you don't understand something properly yourself, you cannot explain it to someone else. Attempting to do so clarifies thought.

Differentiation: As above.

Extension: Challenge children to make an amusing 'push-along' toy for a toddler.

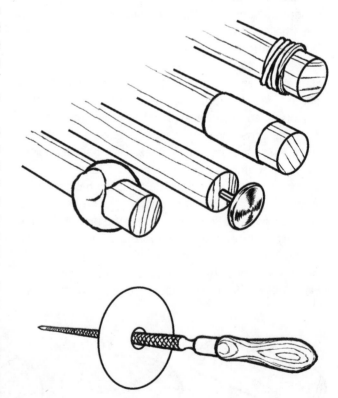

112

DESIGN AND TECHNOLOGY

Structures (1): striking sounds

Investigate

You will need: a tuning fork, a saucepan or similar lid, a bowl of water and a beater.

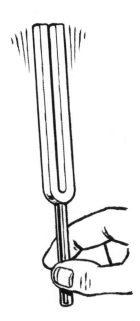

● Strike the tuning fork firmly (not too hard) on the edge of a wooden table. Stand it on the table. Listen to the sound it makes. How does it make this sound?

_____

● Strike the tuning fork again but this time dip it into a bowl of water. What happens? Can you explain why?

_____

● Hold the edge of the saucepan lid and strike it with the beater. Now suspend the lid and listen to the sound that it makes when you strike it. Is there a difference? Why?

_____

Invent

We have called this instrument a 'coat-clanger'.

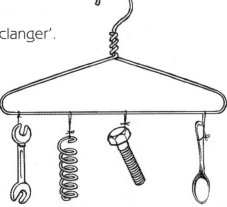

Here are some other 'clangers' we have invented.

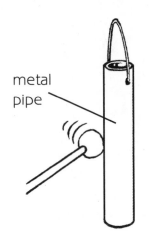

metal
pipe

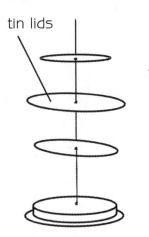

tin lids

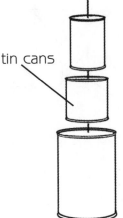

tin cans

● Design and make your own clanger instrument. Make sure that it is a quality instrument that will produce sounds that you can control. Give it a suitable name.

Structures (2): tunes from tubes

Investigate

You will need: a piece of flexible hose (garden, shower or washing machine) at least 60cm long, card and sticky tape.

● Blow a raspberry with your lips pushed together (make a long juicy 'p' sound). Make your lips vibrate like a reed in an instrument.
● Put your lips against one end of the hose and blow your raspberry again.
● Tighten and loosen your lips to alter the sound. How many different sounds can you make?

Invent

We have called this one a 'raspberry blower's funnel-snake'.

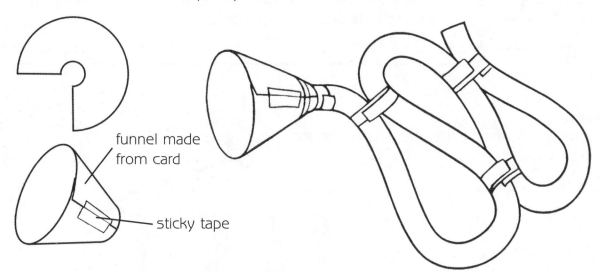

funnel made from card

sticky tape

Here are some other ideas for making a wind instrument using a tube.

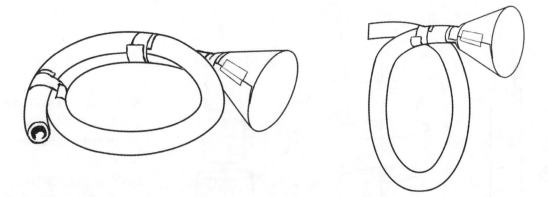

● Design and make your own instrument using a tube and a funnel. If you can, put a trumpet mouthpiece in the end. What difference does it make? Can you change the note the instrument produces? Give your instrument a suitable name.

Using your loaf (1)

● Add to this list of bread products.

soft white	wholemeal	soda	pitta

ciabatta

● Keep a record of how much bread or bread products you eat in a week. Compare your results with a friend.

● Try out this basic bread recipe.

What to do

1. Mix flour, salt and yeast in a large bowl.

2. Make a well in the centre and add the oil and warm water.

Ingredients
400g strong white bread flour
3tbsp oil
7g active dried yeast
1tsp salt
250ml warm water

3. Mix to make a soft dough (add a little more water if too dry) – a round bladed knife may be used.

4. On a lightly floured surface, knead until the dough is smooth and elastic (about 10 minutes).

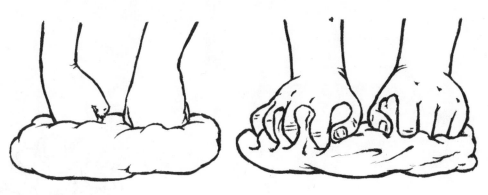

5. Place in a large lightly oiled bowl, cover with clingfilm and leave for about an hour until the dough has doubled in size.

6. Bake at 200°C for 35–40 minutes.

Using your loaf (2)

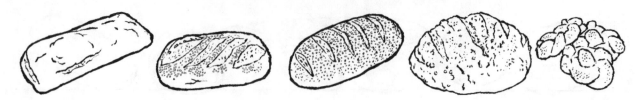

Investigate
● Look at the bread recipe on the last sheet. Try it again but make changes. Plan your changes before you start and write them down. Don't change too many things at once! Check with your teacher that your plan is fine and that the ingredients are available.

Some ideas
● Use a different flour (rye, wholemeal, chapatti).

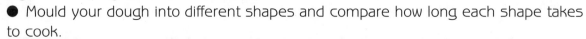

● Add or replace ingredients (sugar, milk, fruit, butter).
● Mould your dough into different shapes and compare how long each shape takes to cook.
● Add a topping (cheese, flour, nuts, sugar, milk).

Invent
● Adapt the basic bread recipe and design and make a new bread product for a party. Write out the recipe below. List the ingredients, the stages, the quantities and the cooking time. How much will it cost?

Mechanisms (1): moving along

Investigate

● Draw a circle of radius 3cm on card. Cut it out. (You will find it useful to make more than one.)

● The challenge is to make your card circle move unaided in a straight line. Add any materials you wish that will enable the circle to roll down a slope in a straight line (without being pushed at the beginning).

> A **cam** changes rotary movement into movement in a straight line.

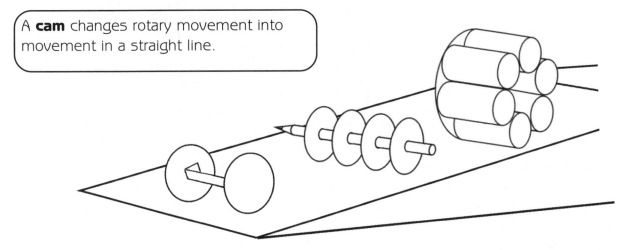

● What is the cam in your mechanism?

_____

● Here are some ideas to try.

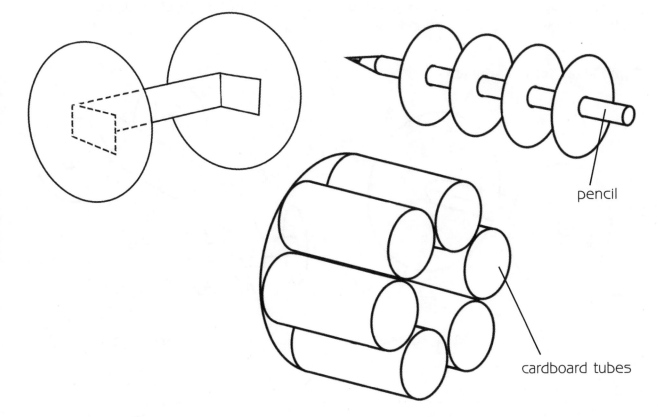

pencil

cardboard tubes

◢SCHOLASTIC 117

Mechanisms (2): moving around

Here are different ways of fixing wheels onto axles.

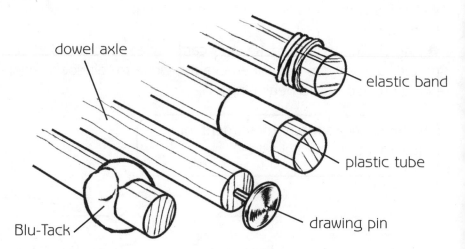

The axle hole can be filed for a loose fit.

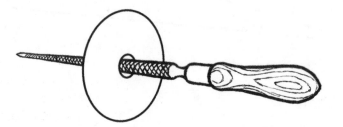

● Using any materials available, make a **Rollaround** using a cam mechanism that will enable a wheel to turn a corner as it rolls down a slope. You may need to use one of the methods above for your Rollaround machine.

Some ideas for Rollarounds

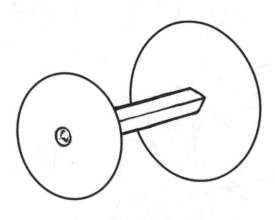

unequal wheels joined by an axle

a steering arrangement

● Describe how your mechanism works to a friend.

ICT

The curriculum for Year 5 requires both specific expertise and specified equipment, both computer hardware and software. You will need controlling devices (control boxes and software), sensors, object-based graphic packages and spreadsheets as well as the skills to handle all of them. On the whole, the challenge for both teacher and children is to acquire sufficient practice at operating the software that they can forget the mechanics and focus on the intellectual element. If you find that the mechanics comes between you and the real curriculum content then you should seek to acquire the necessary skills and practice through in-service training of some sort.

The sheets in this section focus on activities consistent with aims set down within some of those units in the QCA Scheme of Work but it was not possible or practical to cover all the topics. We have focused on Unit 5A 'Graphical modelling', Unit 5D 'Introduction to spreadsheets' and Unit 5E 'Controlling devices'. As hardware is likely to be in great demand, there are classroom management issues here if a whole class is to cover a worksheet. You are most unlikely to have one control box per child, for example, and none of the activities are suitable for groups to tackle. There is work that can be done 'off-screen' and you should take advantages of these opportunities to free up hardware for other children to use.

Manipulating models (page 121)

Objective: To use an object-based graphics package to manipulate shapes.

What to do: Here children are directed to design a play area using computer 'models' constructed from lines, circles and so on which can be manipulated to alter and improve the design. This obviously requires an object-based graphics package. You will need to show children how to create graphic models using the software. Sketching can be done off-screen to free up computer time but the final design must be computer-based. You may wish to use an area plan that relates to a real area within the school grounds.

Differentiation: Direct less computer literate children to practise by making an abstract design, moving, resizing and rotating graphic elements to create interesting patterns. Some children will need more time and practice at this than others.

Extension: The children

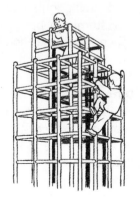

could work to scale. They can, for example, relate the size of equipment to one specific piece, such as making the slide twice the size of the tunnel.

Spreadsheet scoreboard
(page 122)

1	2 1st Test	3 2nd Test	4 3rd Test	5 Average
2 Ganguly	43	10	132	61.66667
3 Sehwag	71	61	23	51.66667
4 Dravid	73	88	66	75.66667
5 Singh	64	101	0	55
6 Kaif	14	8	31	17.66667
7 Total	265	268	252	

Objective: To enter data into cells on a spreadsheet, modify data and check results.

What to do: Check that the children know what rows, columns and cells are. Remind them how to enter data on a spreadsheet – they will need to be able to enter data and label columns and rows. They will also need to know how to calculate an average and how to do so on a spreadsheet. If you have not already taught it, then demonstrate the short way of making totals using *AutoSum* and also how to calculate averages using *Paste Function*. This is a challenging activity so supervise closely the initial work to see that the spreadsheet is set up properly. Answers: Dravid has the best average at 75.7 (rounded up to one decimal place); the Second Test had the highest total score for the five batsmen at 268 runs.
If the error is corrected, Ganguly now becomes the batsman with the highest average (91.7) but the second Test remains the highest scoring match.

Differentiation: If you have the facilities, demonstrate the first steps in the process on an OHP. You may find it necessary to get some children started by providing the headings and basic structure. This is really differentiation by the amount of support offered.

Extension: Once children know how to use formulae to carry out calculations, you could challenge them to set up a spreadsheet that will hold data on a number of circles (circumference and diameter) and then calculate the ratio of one to the other (p = c ÷ d). What do they notice about the results?

The cheapest school trip
(page 123)

Objective: To create and use a spreadsheet to produce costings.

What to do: This sheet presupposes a reasonable

competence at setting up and using a spreadsheet. Children will need to know how to enter formulae to fill in the missing data. The problem is quite a tricky one as children need to alter data to answer the last two questions. Check that children have set up the spreadsheet correctly before they tackle the four questions posed. Travel costs must be worked out in £ not pence otherwise bizarre results will be achieved. The cheapest trip is to Norfolk (£98.33 per child) and the most expensive to Broadstairs (£140.70 per child). Abolishing excursions does not alter the answers to question 1 and 2 but does reduce costs, especially to Broadstairs. Likewise changing to the cheaper travel company does not affect the overall result although prices are reduced. Hotel costs would be the most significant element in pricing a trip but which trip children choose may be justified on any logical grounds. Cost is not the only factor!

Differentiation: A degree of competence is required but you can reduce the challenge for the less able by setting up the structure first and by reducing the sophistication required (for example, ignore currency sign).

Extension: Children can produce their own extension work by suggesting other situations in which the use of a spreadsheet might be beneficial. Challenge them to think of one (at home or school). Ask them to think of something that might be of use to them – pocket money accounts perhaps. They could design such a sheet for homework and work to produce the sheet and calculations in school.

Controlling devices (page 124)

Objective: To recognise that control technology is all around us and that devices can be controlled through direct instruction.

What to do: This sheet can be tackled without resorting to the use of a computer. Perhaps the best way to start is by a general class discussion about controlling devices. *What are they? What do we mean by a sequence of instructions?* (For example, a sequence of instructions must be fed into the computer to switch on the crossing lights in sequence.) Possible examples of other devices may include burglar alarms, car door locks, automatic cooker timers, and so on.

Differentiation: Group work is desirable for those children who find this activity challenging. Demonstration of devices (using a pelican crossing, for example) is worthwhile if you can arrange it.

Extension: *What advantages do machines have over human beings in operating simple devices? For example, is it better to have someone operating the car barrier or to have it operate automatically? Would flashing lights be better than a crossing patrol?* Ask children to discuss these issues giving pros and cons.

Taking control (page 125)

Objective: To understand that control box software can be used to control an output device.

What to do: For this activity you will need a control box with the appropriate software, a light, a buzzer and the necessary switches and connections. The sheet illustrates one such device and, depending on which set-up you have, there are variations from the illustrations shown. However, the basic language and principles do not vary and you should simply check that the sheet does not significantly misrepresent your equipment such that it misleads your children. In previous years children will have used LOGO and consequently should know how to edit their procedures. Children's work should begin with connecting the light bulb to the control box. You should make all other connections before the children start.

The results are self-marking. Either the procedure does what it sets out to do or it doesn't. Children should edit their procedure until they produce the required result.

Differentiation: Confidence as well as know-how is the key here and you can help children by giving them the mutual support of a partner. However, you will need to make sure that one child does not 'take over' to the exclusion of the other. Ask the children to read out the procedure to their partner before they type it into the computer. *Does it sound right?* Obvious errors are usually self-corrected in this way.

Extension: The next sheet can be used as extension work, but more able children can construct models of some sophistication that are controlled by computers. When they have mastered the basic skills, challenge them to create a sequence of instructions that control a number of output devices. Challenges might include barriers, lights, bridges, lifts, buzzers, pressure pads and so on. The challenge should match the ability of your children. If in doubt consult your subject coordinator or adviser.

Controlling traffic lights (page 126)

Objective: To use simple control language to activate multiple devices concurrently.

What to do: At this stage you should build the home-made traffic lights yourself to demonstrate how such a system can be constructed. Children can then concentrate on writing the control language, which is the main object of the exercise. (Check: SWITCH OFF 3 2 is not SWITCH OFF 32.)

Differentiation: Once again you should not leave less able children to tackle this alone. Reading out the sequence to each other first helps, but children should be allowed time to succeed by 'trial and success'.

Extension: See extension notes for 'Taking control', above.

Manipulating models

Imagine that the headteacher has put you in charge of planning a new play area in the corner of the school field. Use your computer to create a plan. Here is some of the apparatus you might wish to include. Make models of them on the screen using shapes and lines, moving them around to make the best arrangement.

First, draw a pencil sketch of your plan here.

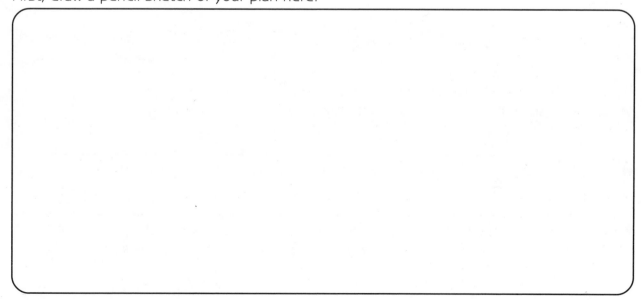

Spreadsheet scoreboard

columns

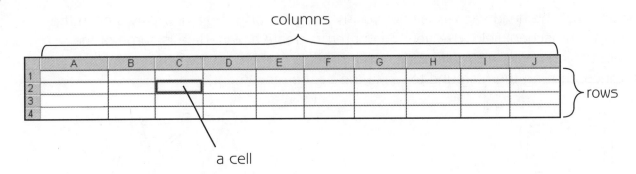

a cell

rows

The scores of the five main batsmen in a cricket Test Match are quoted in the newspaper article below. Create a spreadsheet to show their scores in the three matches. Put the data into the correct cells. Use SUM **Σ** to find totals and insert a column to calculate the batsmen's average scores.

Test Match Review

In the first Test Ganguly scored 43 runs, Sehwag 71, Dravid 73, Singh 64 and Kaif 14. In the high scoring second Test Singh made 101 runs, Kaif only 8, Dravid a splendid 88, Sehwag 61 and Ganguly 10. But the third Test brought the best out of Ganguly who made 132 before he was caught on the boundary. Sehwag made 23, Dravid 66, but Singh was out for a duck although Kaif made 31.

Use your spreadsheet to find out:
● Which batsman had the best run average?

_____

● In which Test did the five batsmen's combined scores make the highest total?

_____

● If the scorer had made an error and recorded Ganguly's score as 10 in the second Test when it should have been 100, would it make any difference to your answers?

_____

The cheapest school trip

Set up the spreadsheet below to handle the costings for a proposed residential school trip. There is a choice of five possible places to visit. There are 25 children going on the trip. The school's favourite coach company charges 11.5p per mile, per child, for the journey.

● Use formulae to calculate the data for the blank cells.

	A	B	C	D	E	F	G	H	I	J
1	Places	Miles	Travel cost (per child)	Travel cost (total)	Hotel cost (per child)	Hotel cost (total)	Excursions (per child)	Excursions (total)	Overall (per child)	Overall (total cost)
2	Broadstairs			£517.50		£2,550	£18			
3	Isle of Wight			£345.00		£2,125	£6			
4	Norfolk			£388.13		£1,875	£7.80			
5	Snowdonia			£235.75		£2,225	£8			
6	Whitby			£603.75		£1,975	£15.50			

● Now use the spreadsheet to find out:
– the cheapest trip

_____

– the most expensive trip.

_____

● Cut out all trips and museum visits. Does it change your last two answers?

_____

● The Shoestring Coach Company offers to transport the children for 6p per mile per child. What difference does this make to your answers?

_____

● Which trip would you choose? Explain your choice.

_____

● Which factor has the biggest influence on the cost of the trip?

_____

_____

Controlling devices

Some everyday devices rely on simple control features to make them work. Some devices require only one instruction.

● What makes this barrier operate? _____

_____

_____

Other devices require a sequence of instructions to operate..

● What happens here?

_____

_____

_____

_____

_____

● Think of other devices at home, in school, in the high street, that operate on instructions. Fill in this chart with examples.

Device	single instruction	sequence of instructions

Taking control

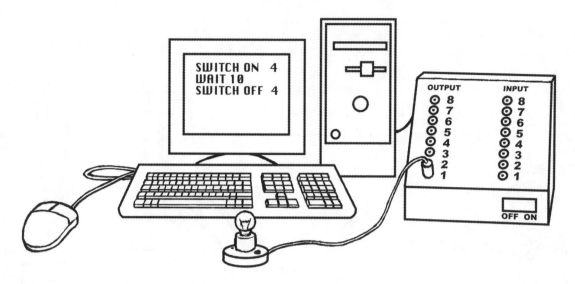

● Connect a light bulb to one end of a control box lead and put the jack plug into output socket 1.

The light can be switched off and on using control language and the control box software.

SWITCH ON	1	(turns the light on)
SWITCH OFF	1	(turns the light off)

● Put the jack plug into output socket 3. What commands would be needed to switch the light on and off now? Write them down.

_____

_____

_____

● Using the command WAIT, try a sequence of instructions before the enter key is pressed so that the light stays on for a certain number of seconds before being switched off. Write them down.

_____

_____

_____

● Connect a buzzer to another output socket. Write a procedure for the light bulb and the buzzer to operate in short bursts.

_____

_____

_____

Controlling traffic lights

● Here are some home-made traffic lights connected to a control box. Make a similar set and connect to a control box connected to a computer.

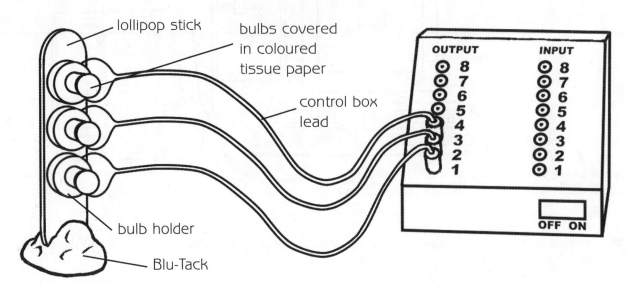

lollipop stick

bulbs covered in coloured tissue paper

control box lead

bulb holder

Blu-Tack

OUTPUT   INPUT

● Can you write a procedure using control language that will operate the lights in the correct sequence? We have started the procedure for you.

SWITCH ON 3 _____   _____

WAIT 3 _____   _____

SWITCH ON 2 _____   _____

WAIT 3 _____   _____

SWITCH OFF 3   2 _____   _____

● Try it out. Make changes if necessary.
● If you give the procedure a name such as FLASH, you can now REPEAT your procedure and the traffic lights will continue to operate. Try it!

REPEAT 10 _____

FLASH _____

END _____

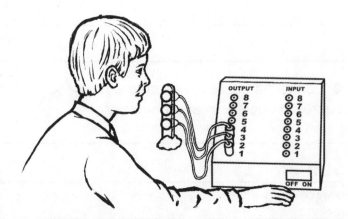

ART AND DESIGN

© COREL

If there is any subject that does not fit easily into a timetable, it is art and design. A weekly dose of 'art' tends to become a 'weakly' dose. Creative work of any sort usually takes 'as long as it takes', although even great artists sometimes had to work to deadlines. The QCA Scheme of Work has a time requirement of between 32 and 45 hours and as with many of the QCA time estimates, this represents a rise over the previous year. There is no simple answer to the time problem, although looking for cross-curricular links is the standard solution. The comedian Spike Milligan, castigated for arriving late at the Army Recruiting Office, offered 'to fight nights as well.' We wouldn't dream of suggesting this sort of overtime but creative work can sometimes continue voluntarily at break-times and after school. The tasks in this section will help to underpin the approaches suggested in the QCA scheme. If you wish to study this in more detail consult www.standards.dfee.gov.uk/schemes.

Some of the artists quoted in the scheme are modern practitioners who have not always reached a status where they can be found in standard reference books so we suggest that the Internet may be your best (possibly your only) resource (try www.artnet.com). We have included references where we can. One obvious drawback to our photocopiable sheets is the lack of colour but we have been able to cover a great deal even so. However you must provide the experience of colour, especially where the study of other artists' work is involved. Reproductions are excellent these days and you should consider including a visit to a gallery in your schedule for the year.

'Art and design is not just a subject to learn, but an activity that you can practise with your hands, your eyes, your whole personality.' Thus is quoted Quentin Blake (illustrator) in the National Curriculum, a quotation that puts the Key Stage 2 approach to art and design in a nutshell. It is not just a matter of what children must do, but what they need to experience. Children must examine and question the work of creative people whether they are artists, designers, architects or sculptors, so there is clearly plenty of art and design 'fieldwork' for children to do. They should also start to compile a portfolio of their own work and in particular, they should build up a record of their observations by using a sketchbook, a record that should follow them through their junior school years.

Still life (1) (page 130)

Objective: To compare and comment on ideas, methods and approaches used in still-life paintings.

What to do: This sheet should not be the starting point for work on still life; children will need to be used to looking at pictures, discussing them and using the terminology required before tackling the sheet. *What is a* technique? *What is* contrast? Composition? Line? Texture? They will be able to build upon their work in previous years, for example on *viewpoints*, but they may need reminding. Unless children become used to 'hard looking', focusing fully on a picture, then the answers to the questions on the sheet are likely to be superficial. Children should be shown a range of still-life paintings in colour. The best way of doing this, other than visiting the world's galleries, is to use coloured photographic (or OHP) slides. Your school should, ideally, build up a collection perhaps culled from galleries that teachers have visited. Visit www.nationalgallery.org.uk or www.abcgallery.com to look for sources.

Both this sheet and the next, which is provided as an extra resource, are best 'talked through' as a class or group activity; children will then be better equipped to tackle the questions asked. Provide extra sheets of paper for children to write their answers

Differentiation: This is a difficult sheet for a lone child, especially one without well-developed language skills. Let those who would clearly benefit work on this task in a group. You may also like to enlarge the sheet to assist examination. Alternatively, translate the sheet into an OHP transparency.

Extension: Move on to look at similarities and differences. For this you will need to provide at least two decent still-life images. We have provided an additional image on the next sheet. Perhaps there are some hanging up in the school? Ask children to compare and comment on the methods and ideas used in the two paintings. Ask children to find a still-life picture that they particularly like (for homework perhaps) and to explain to the class why they like it.

Still life (2) (page 131)

© COREL

Objective: To compare and comment on ideas, methods and approaches used in still-life paintings.

What to do: This is a companion to the last sheet and follows on from it. The answer to the first question is *still life*. The approach should be as suggested above, although you do have the opportunity to use the two sheets together and to make comparisons. Comparison should still focus on the areas covered by the worksheet. As before, provide extra paper for answers.

Differentiation: See 'Still life (1)'.

Extension: Ask children to produce their own 'still life'. (See 'Still life DIY', below.)

Still life DIY (page 132)

Objectives: To select and record a still life from first-hand observation; to make a number of small studies that explore different ideas.

What to do: Remind children of the study of still-life work by well-known artists that they have already covered before they begin. The sheet can be used with little preparation although children will need their sketchbooks and ultimately the paper and paint needed to paint a picture. You should manage this so that only small groups reach the painting stage at any one time. Clearly this is not a whole-class activity. Provide a few interesting additions to the usual classroom setting if you can – an unusual vase, a colourful drape, flowers, a variety of desk tidies, and so on.

Differentiation: As there are no 'right' answers, differentiation need only be a case of providing sufficient stimulus and encouragement. Take a few photographs of arrangements of classroom objects to demonstrate what sort of still-life pictures might be created. Give less able children time, space, encouragement and not too many objects to work with.

Extension: Talk to each child individually about their picture just as you would discuss their maths work. Have they achieved what they set out to do? How might they have improved their picture? Look for positive, creative comments rather that criticism. Encourage them to talk about the choices they made and how these choices influenced their final picture. Create a class 'Gallery of Still Life' and display the work. You will have your own views on displaying work, indeed the school may have a distinct policy. Some display all work, some select, some feel that children's work should be cherished and therefore displayed with great care by teachers (double mounted and so on).

Urn, vessel, basket and pot (page 133)

Objectives: To explore the tradition of making containers; to consider the work of contemporary designers of vessels; to create and decorate a container.

What to do: Introduce this topic by creating a display of different types of container. Include some that are purely decorative. Ask children to identify them and think about function, how they were made and whether they 'work'. This is a good opportunity to include articles of ethnic or historical origin (Greek vases, for example) even if only in photographic form. The sheet itself is best undertaken by pairs of children or small groups, as this will encourage discussion. The work shown here is by children; work by the contemporary ceramicists recommended by the QCA is not readily accessible, mainly because it is contemporary, but you can consult the Internet for pictures and information, for example www.craftscouncil.org.uk, www.british-museum.ac.uk, www.caa.org.uk, www.galeriebesson.co.uk and www.bluedeco.com/bordeaux/katemalone.

The missing words are *container* and *contemporary*. The 'make a container' activity has been left deliberately open although we had in mind that the children would make, fire, decorate and glaze their own pottery. We are aware that some schools still lack the facilities for doing this although progressive areas have encouraged clay work in primary schools for many decades. Consult your subject coordinator for help. We have found that local secondary schools are usually only too pleased to offer kiln facilities for projects like this. Some expertise is needed (although this is not about throwing pots on a wheel) and you should take advice if you lack it. Containers can, of course, be made from a range of other materials – papier-mâché, textiles, card and natural materials.

Differentiation: This is one of those cases where differentiation will be largely by outcome, however, the use of only vaguely understood terms can be a barrier to less able children. Make sure that there is an adult on-hand to explain words and questions to those whose comprehension is less than complete.

Extension: Exciting possibilities present themselves. You have the opportunity to get children all fired-up about ceramics (excuse the pun). Children will not only enjoy doing but also seeing these things done. Collect photographs of 'mum's favourite pot' (or similar). Visit a local gallery. Get the school to invest in a piece of pottery (perhaps purchased from a local art college end-of-year exhibition) and involve children in the choice (we ourselves have done this successfully). Encourage a local potter to visit the school and talk about his work.

Textile tales (page 134)

Objective: To identify and comment on the content, ideas and ways that stories are communicated visually using textiles.

What to do: This is a straightforward interrogation of pictures in the first instance but should lead children to focus on the way in which stories are communicated visually. Either before or after using this sheet you could look at illustrations in a variety of forms (book illustrations for example). Ideally you should show an example of a textile picture to the class.

Differentiation: This is another activity that could usefully be done in a group. Less able children will gain support and ideas working in this way but it could benefit all children.

Extension: Examine the connection between stories and pictures. This is probably best done by looking at story-book illustrations. *How has the artist conveyed the atmosphere of the story in her pictures? What techniques has she used? How successful has she*

been? Ask children to choose a favourite book illustration and to explain their choice to the class.

Tell a terrible tale in textiles
(page 135)

Objective: To make a collaborative textile work that tells a story.

What to do: The objective, as stated, is to produce something collaboratively. This means making decisions collectively as a class. First ask the children to read the story – you might wish to act it out in drama or dance. Then talk with children about the different techniques that they could use to make a textile picture illustrating the story of the Cyclops. Clue words are given on the sheet. You might wish to limit choices (for example, not dye the fabric yourselves) but all this should be discussed openly. Ideally, you should allow children to try out different techniques on a small scale before the final decisions are made. We suggest that you consult books on textile art and have suitable books for children to refer to also. (Use the resources of your Library Service and your subject coordinator.) Having made decisions about precisely what is to be made, how it is to be made, size, colours, textures and so on, you then need to organise the making. You might divide into groups that could work on sections independently, you will certainly wish to involve the help of classroom assistants and you may even go for a whole-class textile-making jamboree. The choice is yours. Although the QCA unit 5C 'Talking textiles' is not sufficient for detailed information on how to do things, it does offer useful suggestions on techniques you can consider for a project of this sort.

Differentiation: As this is a collaborative task you should make sure that less able children are supported by others and that the tasks they are allocated are a reasonable match to their competence to do them.

Extension: Invite a good amateur or a professional textile artist into school to talk to the children and to demonstrate their work.

Still life (1)

© COREL

This painting is called *Apples and Oranges* by Paul Cézanne. We call these sorts of pictures **still life**. Do you think that the name is a good one? Explain your answer.

_____

Subject: Describe what the artist has painted.

_____

Viewpoint: Describe the view the artist has taken. What difference would a closer viewpoint have made?

_____

Contrasts: What contrasts can you see?

_____

_____

3-D: The artist has painted solid objects on flat paper. How has he made them look solid?

_____

Technique: What can you deduce from this picture about the techniques the artist used to paint it? How were different surfaces and textures created?

_____

Still life (2)

© COREL

This is *The Bedroom* by Vincent Van Gogh. What do we call this sort of picture?

_____

Subject: Describe what the artist has painted.

_____

Viewpoint: Describe the view the artist has taken. What difference would a closer viewpoint have made?

_____

Contrasts: What contrasts can you see?

_____

_____

3-D: The artist has painted solid objects on flat paper. How has he made them look solid?

_____

Technique: What can you deduce from this picture about the techniques the artist used to paint it? How were different surfaces and textures created?

_____

Still life DIY

Here are some objects that you might find in your classroom.

● Choose a few objects like these (not too many) and arrange them together carefully for a still-life sketch. What surface will you place them on? Where is the light coming from? What background is there?
● Sketch them in your sketchbook.
● Change the arrangement of the objects, or your viewpoint and make more sketches.
● Choose your favourite sketch and make a painting from it.
– What kind of effect do you want to create?
– What colours will you use?
– Which paint?
– What size brushes?
– What kind of paper?

Urn, vessel, basket and pot

● Find one word that describes 'urn, vessel, basket and pot'.

(Use a thesaurus if necessary.) C _____

● Here are some examples made by some children.

They are called c _____ designs.

● Take each design in turn and answer these questions.
– What materials have been used for this container?
– What do you think it is for?
– Is it functional or decorative?
– Describe how you think it was made.

● Design and make a container. Decide its function first. Will it be purely decorative or have a particular purpose? Decide on the materials you will use. Make sketches and notes before you start.

Textile tales

1.

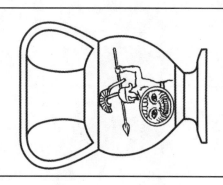

2.

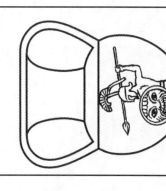

3.

- The pictures on these Greek vases tell stories. Describe what is happening in each case.

- Textiles provide more room for telling a story. The story on this tapestry is a famous one. Describe what is happening. How do you think this was made?

Tell a terrible tale in textiles

Read this story, then make a textile picture to illustrate it.

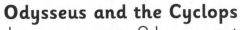

Odysseus and the Cyclops

On his long sea voyage, Odysseus met many terrible monsters, but none worse than the Cyclops. Giant, merciless creatures, they had a big single eye in the centre of their foreheads but spent most of their time as shepherds tending their sheep.

Odysseus landed his ship on the fertile land of the Cyclops and went with his men seeking the people who lived there. Unknowingly, they walked into the cave where lived the Cyclops Polyphemos, although he was out tending sheep at the time. When he returned, he exchanged a few words with Odysseus then picked up several of his men and ate them whole. The Cyclops then blocked the entrance to the cave with a stone that could not be moved.

Odysseus offered Polyphemos a bowl of strong wine to wash down the sailors he had eaten and when the Cyclops was completely drunk and asleep, Odysseus put a desperate plan into operation. With a red-hot stake heated in the fire, Odysseus and his men blinded the Cyclops in his single eye. Wild with pain, the Cyclops was unable to see to kill them.

Later, when Cyclops let the sheep out of the cave, Odysseus and his men escaped by hanging onto the underside of the sheep where the Cyclops could not feel them with his giant hands.

mounting

drawing

sticking

dyeing

knotting

quilting

stitching

printing

sewing

weaving

MUSIC

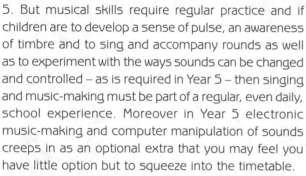

Beyond each worksheet lies music-making, an essential part of the 'listening and performing' that are key elements in the Programme of Study for music for Year 5. But musical skills require regular practice and if children are to develop a sense of pulse, an awareness of timbre and to sing and accompany rounds as well as to experiment with the ways sounds can be changed and controlled – as is required in Year 5 – then singing and music-making must be part of a regular, even daily, school experience. Moreover in Year 5 electronic music-making and computer manipulation of sounds creeps in as an optional extra that you may feel you have little option but to squeeze into the timetable.

The QCA Scheme of Work for music suggests that between 18 and 27 hours be devoted to teaching the subject in Year 5, in which respect music stands out as a subject in which the demands on curriculum time remain unchanged throughout the entire primary years – both at Key Stage 1 and Key Stage 2. Even so this may be an inadequate allocation of time if performance, repetition and practice are taken into account. But music-making can occur in small corners of the timetable – at the end of the day, before assembly, in assembly and so on – and all this time is valuable.

Subject-specific skills and knowledge are required increasingly, by the teacher, as one moves further up the school. Up to a point this is the same for every subject but you should not be reticent in approaching your music coordinator for professional advice and support. You cannot be expected to know everything!

Space odyssey (page 138)

Objective: To identify contrasting moods and sensations and to explore different sound textures.

What to do: You cannot do this sheet cold. You need to encourage children to use the kind of expressive language required. *What would it be like to blast off into outer space in a rocket? What emotions would you feel?* Then ask them to think about the kind of sounds that would match the events, the feelings and emotions that make up the space odyssey. Children may add to the words used to describe the sounds on the sheet. Demonstrate what a relaxed sound is like and what a tight, tense sound is like. Children write down their descriptive words in the spaces provided. They should not be limited to one word per event. Take off could be explosive, fearful, and powerful.

The sheet says 'use any instruments' but you may wish to limit this to untuned instruments.

Differentiation: For those children who need help with language, provide them with thesauruses. Stress to the children that they need to produce musical, controlled sounds that evoke the event.

Extension: Groups of children could write compositions called 'Space Odyssey' using any form or method they wish to write it in. They could perform in front of the class or for assembly. Keyboards may be used, as may a computer's sound recorder if you have this facility to explore sound.

Harmony or agony? (page 139)

Objective: To explore the effects of different combinations of pitched notes using appropriate language.

What to do: Tell the children they are going to learn about harmony. You might demonstrate the value of harmony by playing the harmony to a song or hymn minus the melody and vice versa. Children can proceed to do the sheet alone and unaided but singing the scale as a class is a good idea. The answers are by trial and success. You can test out the children's choices on a different instrument – piano, keyboard and so on. Do all the class agree with the answers? (There are no right or wrong answers, although notes next to each other will be recognised as discords.)

Differentiation: You can only help children by giving them plenty of practice at listening and by giving them the language to describe what they hear. Let the unsure use the words *relaxed* and *comfortable* in preference to *concord* and *clashing* in preference to *discord*.

Extension: Let children explore combinations of three notes from the scale. What different effects can they produce? Do we all 'hear' sounds in the same way?

Send round a fireman (page 140)

Objective: To sing a simple round in two parts and accompany it with a three-note chord (triad).

What to do: You cannot sing a round on your own! There are individual activities on the sheet but music-making is often a social activity and it is on this occasion. Teach the class the round. You will have children who can play this on the recorder or flute (the setting is easy). Children should learn and remember the tune; piano accompaniment is not essential. Stick to singing the round in two groups initially (A and B or A and C). Children should practise with a partner to coordinate the playing of the chord to a steady pulse (either the first beat in every bar or beats 1 and 3). There will need to be some classroom management so that some children are playing chords whilst others are singing. Sing in unison while the drone is played and then try it while the round is being sung. Practice makes perfect.

Differentiation: This is a social activity where differentiation is not desirable. You may wish to hold the hands of those children who have difficulties finding the pulse and beat out the pulse with them until they can feel it for themselves.

Extension: Develop the song into a 'party piece'. You could have a number of children playing chords on different instruments, playing on different beats (1 and 3; only on 1), or even attempt singing the round in the full four parts – each group coming in a line at a time. You should sing the round through at least twice and end either by each group repeating the last line, when they have finished, until all are singing the last line, or have each group drop out as they finish their last line.

Ostinato, drone and melody
(page 141)

Objective: To accompany a round with repeated chords and ostinati.

What to do: Children will need tuned percussion instruments for this exercise. They should perform the sequence of notes given in (1) to (7), and decide whether they are ostinati or drones. (Playing the same chord over and over again is a drone; a constantly repeated sequence of notes is an ostinato.) The ostinati and drones can each be used to accompany the round 'Send round a fireman' used on the previous sheet. The sheet deliberately uses different ways of recording the sequences as a puzzle. We have used 'walk' as shorthand to represent a crotchet and 'run-ning' to represent two quavers to the time of one crotchet. Children will need clever hands or the help of a friend to play the last chord (7). Answers: **1.** drone, **2.** ostinato, **3.** ostinato, **4.** ostinato, **5.** ostinato, **6.** drone, **7.** drone.

Differentiation: Some children may struggle with getting the rhythm of the words. Work with them in a small group, repeating the words with them rhythmically.

Extension: Use different-pitched instruments to provide this accompaniment. Only the notes should be played not the mnemonics given with them. Don't forget the singers!

Open and closed (page 142)

Objective: To identify and control different ways in which percussion instruments make sounds.

What to do: The illustrations demonstrate open and closed sounds using a triangle. You might wish to demonstrate this or let the children try it for themselves. Have they noticed the different method used to play the instrument in each case? Children could try out the three instruments illustrated (which will need to be readily available in the classroom) – tambourine, drum and cymbal – and add a fourth of their own choice. They should describe the method by which they produced the two types of sound in the spaces provided.

Differentiation: Differentiate by allowing extra time for some children to explore the instruments. You will need to provide time and space for this to minimise disturbance (not to say noise pollution). You cannot simply shut children away in a soundproofed room to get on with it (however much you might wish to do so!). Use a classroom assistant to supervise and a suitable place where the sounds produced will not be too intrusive.

Extension: Teach the children correct ways of producing different sounds on percussion instruments. This should be linked to teaching them to value and look after instruments. Do they know how to keep it silent when they do not wish it to produce a sound? How should it be stored and where? You may wish to venture into the extensive world of percussion instruments – there are many that have associations with different cultures. Perhaps you can get in experts to provide a demonstration?

Keeping the pulse (page 143)

Objective: To improvise rhythmic patterns to a steady pulse.

What to do: Children should have plenty of practice at repeating rhythmic patterns to a steady pulse. For example, clap and say a four-beat pulse (*Who is in class?*). Point to a child. The class then reply (whilst you continue clapping or beating the pulse) *Em-ma is in class* (substitute the name of the child). And so on. This sheet works on the same principle. We have assumed that children will use notation to record the rhythms but you may choose not to require them to use this method.

Differentiation: Less confident children might work in a small group under adult supervision to clap out the rhythms.

Extension: You can create a cacophony of traffic, a veritable M25 of sound, each group or individual repeating the vehicular rhythm perhaps with suitable pitched accompaniment. The pulse could be beaten out on a big drum or tom-toms. Have a conductor who can exclude some traffic, have the noise fade away to Sunday-morning levels, or wound up to reach a rush-hour crescendo.

Space odyssey

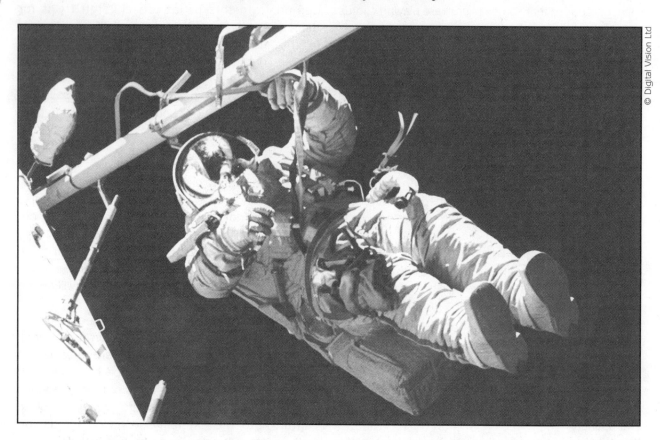

● What musical sounds might you use to describe a journey into space? What kind of sounds would fit the space-journey words below? Describe them.

open

smooth

heavy

Take off _____

Excitement _____

Fear _____

Weightlessness _____

Awe _____

Beauty _____

Darkness _____

Light _____

relaxed

light

urgent

loose

tight

textured

● Use any instruments to make these sounds. Try to create different moods. Add more sounds; take some away. Explore ways of improving the sounds you use to describe a 'Space Odyssey'.

Harmony or agony?

● Play these chime bars in turn from low C to higher C. Sing each note to 'lah'. Sing using the letter names for the notes. Sing and play!

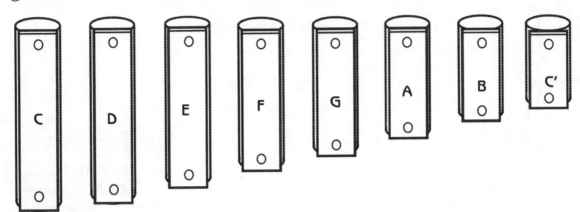

● This is called a scale. Sing up the scale C to C'. Sing down the scale C' to C.

● Choose any two chime bars from the scale above and play the notes together. How do they sound? Tense? Relaxed? Comfortable? Tight? Loose?

> If they fit easily together then this is called a **concord**. If they don't and the notes seem to argue with each other then this is called a **discord**.

● Try out different combinations of two notes from the scale and record your results.

_____

_____

_____

_____

_____

_____

_____

_____

_____

_____

Send round a fireman

A | I am a fireman with a big hat,
B | Sliding down the pole I land on a mat.
C | Clang, clang! Ding, dong! goes my bell.
D | Put out the fire and all is well.

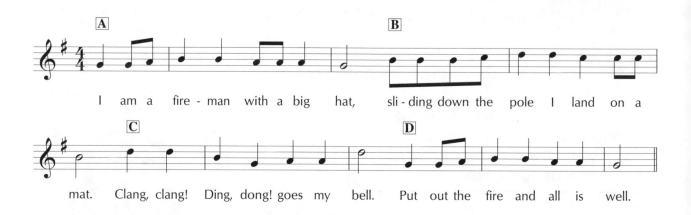

I am a fire-man with a big hat, sli-ding down the pole I land on a

mat. Clang, clang! Ding, dong! goes my bell. Put out the fire and all is well.

● Learn to sing this song. You may be able to play it on your recorder.

● With your teacher's help, sing the song as a round. You can sing in two groups. The second group starts singing from the beginning when the first group reaches **C**.

Accompany the singing

● With a friend play all three of these notes at the same time on a slow, steady pulse while the class sing the round.

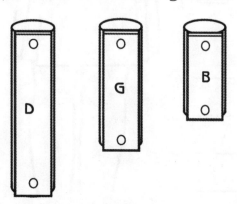

D   G   B

Playing the same chord over and over again like this is called a **drone**.

Ostinato, drone and melody

● Here are various **drones** and **ostinati** written down in different ways. Play them and say which are ostinati and which are drones. You can play them to accompany 'Send round a fireman'.

1. 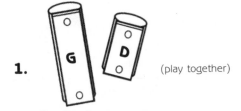 (play together) _____

2. **B B**　　**B**　**C**　**D**　(keep repeating) _____
Slid-ing　down　a　pole

3. **D**　**D**　**B**　**G**　(keep repeating) _____
Clang,　clang!　Ding,　dong!

4. **B**　**B**　**G**　**G**　(repeat at a walk) _____
walk　walk　walk　walk

5. **G G**　　**G G**　　**D D**　　**D D**　(repeat as a running rhythm) _____
run-ning,　run-ning,　run-ning,　run-ning

6.  (play together) _____

7.  (play together) _____

● Play these arrangements with friends while the melody ('Send round a fireman') is being sung.

Open and closed

This makes an open sound.

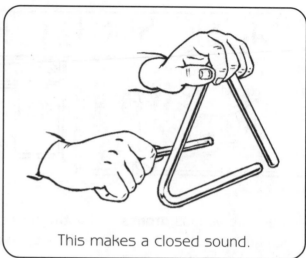

This makes a closed sound.

Explore how to make open and closed sounds with these different instruments. Describe how you did it.

Instrument	Open	Closed
My choice		

Keeping the pulse

On the beat...

Pulse keeper

● Play this pulse on a tambourine.

(walk   walk   walk   walk)

● Make these vehicles keep the pulse.

1.	2.
Big black motor car	High fly-ing jum-bo jet
3.	**4.**
Noi-sy, noi-sy, skateboards	Sleek white am-bu-lance

On the beat...

● Invent some vehicle phrases of your own. Make them 'keep the pulse'. Clap and say them while a friend plays the pulse (walk walk walk walk) on a tambour or drum.

RELIGIOUS EDUCATION

The teaching of RE in primary schools is a *statutory requirement* and must be taught according to a *locally agreed syllabus* in all maintained schools except voluntary-aided and schools of a religious character. In the latter types of school, religion should be taught according to a trust deed or guidelines.

Agreed syllabuses tend to share common elements and QCA have felt confident enough to produce a scheme of work, even though there is no 'national' curriculum around which it might fit. Because religion is closely bound up in strongly held beliefs, faith communities and cultural heritage, the syllabuses that emerge from QCA and local SACREs (Standing Advisory Committees on Religious Education) can sometimes sit uneasily with maturation levels of children. In their formulation they need to satisfy many demands, expectations and pressures.

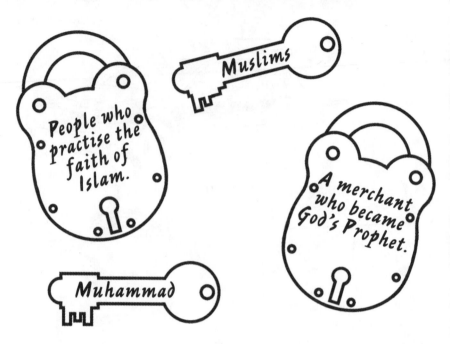

For children in Year 5, religious education can be quite demanding in terms of knowledge if we take the QCA scheme as an exemplar of primary RE schemes. Of course your area may have chosen to study different faiths at this level but we have kept to Islam and Christianity, in line with the QCA's choices. A time allocation of 24 hours is suggested which, interestingly, is less than in Year 3 (30 hours).

It is recommended that where questions arise about a particular faith community rather than general matters then advice might be best sought from members of that faith community themselves.

Islam: key words (page 147)

Objective: To identify basic religious beliefs of Muslims about Allah, Muhammad and the Qur'an (Koran).

What to do: This is a text-heavy sheet with some difficult words that may be new to children. If it is used in the context of a project on Islam then it should pose no difficulty, otherwise you may wish to read and discuss the text with the children. The key words can be linked to the statements by colour matching, by linking with a line, or by cutting out the keys and statements and sticking them together correctly. The answers are self-evident but can be checked with reference to the text.

At some point during your study of Islam you should make children aware of the respect with which Muslims treat matters related to their faith. The Koran (Qur'an) is never placed on the floor or under other books and the words of the Koran are never changed (because they are the words of God) which is why Muslims learn Arabic in order to understand them. When Muslims say the Prophet Muhammad's name (and when writing), they follow it with the words 'peace and blessings of Allah upon him'. The latter phrase is 'Salla-llahu alaihi wa sallam' and the letters SAW are used in English translations. A specific symbol in Arabic is also used.

For further information there are many books for teachers and children that can be consulted. *This is Islam*, Michael Keene, (Stanley Thorne), although written for Key Stage 3 children is an accessible reference book for primary teachers in a hurry. The Shap Working Party on World Religions in Education, 36 Causton Street, London SW1P 4AU, offers resources and advice. Artefacts, CD-ROMs, charts and so on are available from Articles of Faith Ltd, Resource House, Kay Street, Bury, BL9 6BU. You should also find the Religious Education Exchange Centre at www.re-xs.ucsm.ac.uk and www.islam101.com useful.

Differentiation: What will differentiate between children here is literary ability, not religious knowledge. Less able children will almost certainly flounder over words, not just the words in bold, but also words such as *prophet* and *sacred*. As this type of religious language may be outside their usual experience, you will need to check that children understand the words in this context. Support material in the form of books, pictures and even artefacts, should be readily available for children to refer to.

Extension: Further investigation could involve children doing more extensive investigations of their own, perhaps using ICT.

Five pillars (page 148)

Objective: To identify the five pillars of Islam.

What to do: This cannot be attempted without decent resources and reference material for the children to use. (See the suggestions above.) This sheet focuses on fact rather than faith and you may wish to explore further with the children how religious beliefs and practices help people to make sense of puzzling aspects of life and also guide them in how to live their own lives.

Differentiation: Let children work in groups on this research. You might direct which pillar the less able children focus on. Children who have little contact with religion and religious practices may find it easier to explain and understand 'Zakah' for example. Indeed, it could be part of a humanist's creed.

Extension: You should, at some point, ask an adult Muslim to explain some of these things to children (do not overburden Muslim children in your class with this responsibility). A visit to a mosque may be possible. Consult your subject coordinator.

Pilgrimage (page 149)

Objective: To know the events and purpose of the Hajj and to understand the difference between a pilgrimage and an ordinary journey.

What to do: Discuss the notion of pilgrimage with the class first. It is a common event in modern times (Lourdes, the Hajj, Gracelands, Auschwitz), and the children may have heard of Christian pilgrims who were a common sight in the Middle Ages. *Why do people go on pilgrimages?* In essence, it is an external journey for an internal need although these needs can be very different in type and origin. Sorting the statements is an activity intended to focus the children on the facts and to gain some understanding of them. Which category they end up under is not critical although encourage

the children to explain their choices. Cutting and sticking is probably the easiest way to deal with this activity.

Differentiation: This should be a cooperative exercise for less able children. Refer them to the headings frequently to check where each statement might fit.

Extension: Try to get a Muslim who has been on the Hajj to describe his or her experiences. Children could write an imaginative piece 'My diary of the Hajj', describing such a journey. You could explore the practical implications of the Hajj. *How much would it cost? How would I get there?* Consult travel brochures; use ICT. Plan the route and an itinerary.

A special book (page 150)

Objectives: To know that the Bible is the world's best-selling book and to be able to place some facts, people and events relating to it on a timeline; to be able to differentiate dates before and after Jesus.

What to do: The Bible is by a long way the world's bestselling book and the children may not realise this. Discuss the reasons for this (large number of Christians; copies in churches, hotels and homes; large number of languages into which it is translated; value and status of the book itself). The class could research facts and figures about the number of languages into which it is translated and so on. The *Guinness Book of Records* is useful.

Children should already be familiar with the system of dating from their history work. Other systems do coexist alongside AD/BC but mostly in a residual cultural way, such as Chinese years. AD/BC is the international standard. In recent years some writers on religious matters (but not historians), have chosen to set aside the connection with the birth of Christ in deference to other faiths, using BCE (before the common era) and CE instead of AD/BC. However the dates remain unchanged. NB: AD precedes the year number, BC follows it.

Differentiation: For those children who struggle with dates, we suggest that you use a larger date line and run it from left to right in the manner of the number

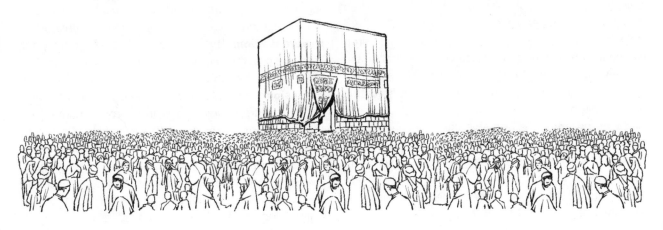

lines with which they will be familiar. You might also divide up centuries to aid date placement.

Extension: You could take any fact or person from the timeline and ask children to find out more for homework. Show children pictures of early Biblical texts. You could investigate illuminated manuscripts (for example, *the Book of Kells*). How did the Bible come to us? This is a big question but it is important to establish that the material of the Bible predates the written text and that it is a collection of writings from different times. Tell the story of the Dead Sea Scrolls.

Resources and information can be obtained from The Westhill Project, Westhill RE Centre, Westhill College, Selly Oak, B29 6LL; Christian Education Movement, Royal Buildings, Victoria Street, Derby, DE3 1GW; www.re-xs.ucsm.ac.uk and www.culham.ac.uk. A good child's book on Christianity is *What do we Know about Christianity?* by Carol Watson, Hodder Wayland, and a fascinating short book about the historical roots of the New Testament (for adults) is *The New Testament Documents, Are They Reliable?* by FF Bruce, Inter-varsity Press.

Belief and action (page 151)

Objective: To identify the link between belief and action and to think about how Christians might apply their beliefs in practical situations.

What to do: This sheet would match well with any activities relating to Christian Aid Week. Focus on events in the news and locally. Neighbours, Christians believe, are any people who need help. Ask children to list places and people from around the world where help is needed. Compare actions that the children suggest with actions that Christians do actually take (for example, local churches collecting blankets and food for the homeless, Christian Aid efforts, Salvation Army Hostels).

Differentiation: Make less able children concentrate on just one 'need for help'. Use a national newspaper cutting of a particular event and ask them to come up with ways in which ordinary Christians could provide help. Let the children work on this as a cooperative activity.

Extension: What other beliefs do Christians have? Interrogate a Christian – not the little old lady from across the road – but the local vicar or similar. Ask the children to make a list of questions to be asked about how Christians put their beliefs (particularly concerning 'love your neighbour') into practice. Alternatively, create a school scenario (theft, vandalism, hate, bullying) and ask children to suggest ways in which a Christian might deal with it. You could act out this scenario as a piece of drama for an assembly.

Love your neighbour (page 152)

Objective: To understand why Christians see all people as neighbours and to begin to understand that stories contain meaning beyond the literal.

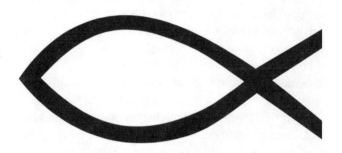

What to do: Provide bibles for children to find the story of the Good Samaritan and read it. Show them how to find chapter and verse. (The Good News Bible is accessible for children.) The text should match the pictures. **1.** The Samaritan is attacked by robbers on the road to Jericho. **2.** A priest walks by even though he is lying half-dead on the roadside. **3.** A lawyer similarly passes by on the other side. **4.** A Samaritan tends to his wounds. **5.** He puts him on his donkey and takes him to an inn. **6.** He pays the bills. Discuss the story with the class. *What point was Jesus making?* The children need to understand that the Samaritan was a foreigner, someone who was generally looked down on, especially by important people such as lawyers and priests.

The fish sign is commonly seen on the boots or rear windows of cars owned by extrovert Christians; a secret sign no longer, more a badge of distinction.

Differentiation: This should be a group activity for less able children and some may need help with finding the story in the Bible.

Extension: You could take another Christian tenet and let the children explore that in a similar manner, for example forgiveness. *Where would Christian forgiveness be helpful? How would it help in world affairs? In school life?* Ask the children to read where forgiveness is mentioned in the Bible, for example The Lord's Prayer (Matthew 16) or the story of the unforgiving servant (Matthew 18: 23–35).

Islam: key words

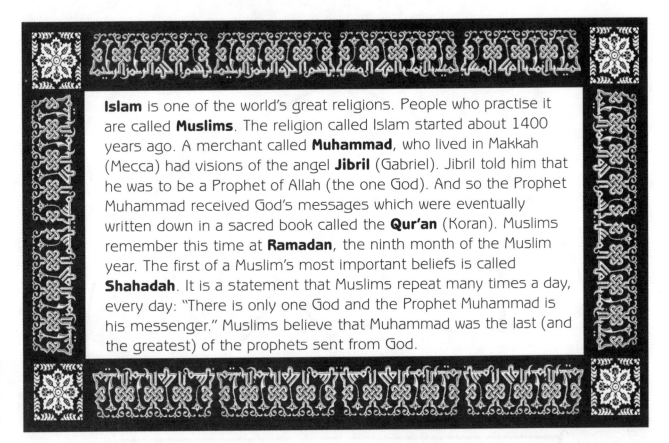

Islam is one of the world's great religions. People who practise it are called **Muslims**. The religion called Islam started about 1400 years ago. A merchant called **Muhammad**, who lived in Makkah (Mecca) had visions of the angel **Jibril** (Gabriel). Jibril told him that he was to be a Prophet of Allah (the one God). And so the Prophet Muhammad received God's messages which were eventually written down in a sacred book called the **Qur'an** (Koran). Muslims remember this time at **Ramadan**, the ninth month of the Muslim year. The first of a Muslim's most important beliefs is called **Shahadah**. It is a statement that Muslims repeat many times a day, every day: "There is only one God and the Prophet Muhammad is his messenger." Muslims believe that Muhammad was the last (and the greatest) of the prophets sent from God.

Fit the keys to the right padlocks.

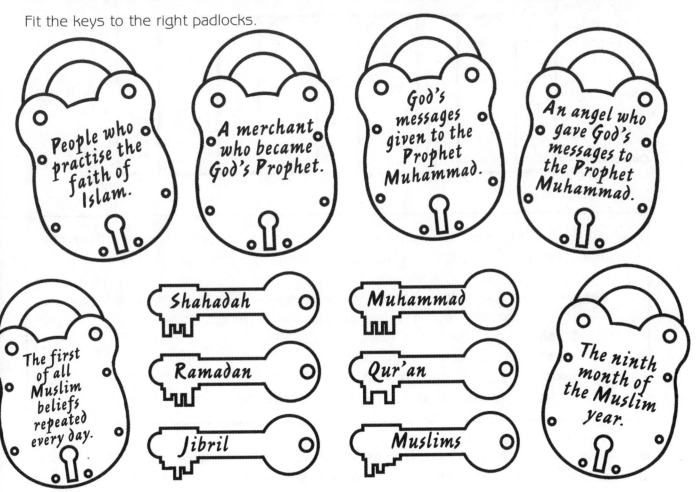

Five pillars

To be a Muslim you must carry out five important religious duties. These are thought of as **'pillars'** because, like pillars holding up a building, they hold up the Muslim faith.

Shahadah   to repeat this important belief every day "There is only one God, Allah and the Prophet Muhammad is his messenger".
Salah   to pray five times a day.
Zakah   to give money to the poor.
Sawm   to fast during Ramadan.
Hajj   to go as a pilgrim to Makkah (Mecca), the holy city.

● Choose one pillar and find out more about it. Explain how Muslims carry out this duty.
● How do duties and rules help us? Talk about this with a friend.

Pilgrimage

● Look up **pilgrimages** in an encyclopedia. List places that people have visited on pilgrimages.

_____

_____

_____

_____

_____

> A **pilgrimage** is a journey with a purpose. Pilgrims usually feel a need, inside themselves, that will only be satisfied by making a special journey. Some old soldiers make pilgrimages to battlefields where their friends were killed in battle. Religious people make journeys to holy places sometimes as a duty.

● A pilgrimage to the holy city **Makkah** (in Saudi Arabia) is one of the five pillars of Islam. It is a duty called the **Hajj**. Sort the following facts under these headings.

Where and when?	Who?	Why?	How?

On the Hajj, Muslims wear similar clothes (men – white, unsewn, cotton sheets and women – plain dresses). | Muslims dress alike on the Hajj to show that they are all the same in the sight of God.

Strict rules apply when they enter the holy city. These are called **ihram**. | Under ihram, pilgrims must not cut their hair or nails or kill any living thing.

Pilgrims also visit Madinah where the Prophet Muhammad is buried. | Every healthy Muslim who can afford it must go on the Hajj.

Muslim pilgrims travel from all over the world. | Under ihram, pilgrims must not wear perfume or jewellery.

The Hajj is a Muslim duty. | The Hajj takes place every year during the 12th month of the Muslim calendar.

The Hajj is a once in a lifetime journey.

A special book

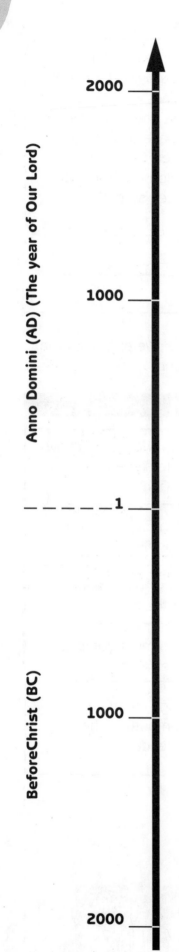

Anno Domini (AD) (The year of Our Lord)

BeforeChrist (BC)

● Which do you think is the world's bestselling book?

_____

● Give two reasons why this might be.

_____

_____

Throughout the world dates are recorded in relation to the birth of Christ. BC is before Christ and AD (anno Domini – in the year of our Lord) is after Christ's birth. But it is difficult to be very accurate about dates a long time ago. We now believe that Christ was born in AD4.

● All these dates are connected to the Bible. Place them on the timeline. (We don't always bother to put AD with a date.)

Abraham **1800BC**	Moses **1200BC**	King David **1000BC**

William Tyndale translated the Bible into English **1526**	Christ's crucifixion **AD30**

First 'authorised' English Bible published **1611**

Greek copies of the New Testament were written on parchment (a codex) – oldest surviving from around **AD350**, the Codex Sinaiticus in the British Museum.

Belief and action

Jesus gave these great commandments to his followers.

1.
Love the Lord your God with all your heart, and with all your soul, and with all your strength, and with all your mind.

PLEASE GIVE

2.
Love your neighbour as you love yourselves.

How might Christians put the second belief into action today? Think about events in the news. Think about your local area. List actions Christians could take.

Who needs help	What Christians could do

Love your neighbour

The first Christians were not always loved. The Romans often tried to kill them.

The Christians used a secret code to avoid being caught. They drew part of a fish in the dust – if the stranger completed it, they knew that the person was a Christian too. The Greek word for fish is ΙΧΘΥΣ.

The letters stood for
ι : Jesus
Χ : Christ
θ : God's
Υ : Son
Σ : Saviour

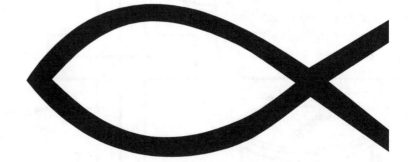

● Where do you see this sign today?

● But Christians were taught to love their neighbour. Who was their neighbour? Jesus taught his followers about neighbours using the story of the Good Samaritan. Read it for yourself (Luke 10: 29–38) and write captions for these pictures.

PSHE AND CITIZENSHIP

You are reminded that PSHE and citizenship are not National Curriculum subjects for Key Stage 1 and Key Stage 2 (citizenship is a statutory requirement at Key Stage 3 and Key Stage 4). Schools are, nevertheless, expected to promote a child's spiritual, moral, social and cultural development, across the National Curriculum.

The knowledge, skills and understanding identified in the *non-statutory framework* for PSHE and citizenship at Key Stage 2 is to be taught under the following headings: 'Developing confidence and responsibility and making the most of their abilities'; 'Preparing to play an active role as citizens'; 'Developing a healthy, safer lifestyle'; 'Developing good relationships and respecting the differences between people'. For Year 5 we have chosen to focus more directly on citizenship (see 'Where am I? Who am I?' and 'People with power – your local authority') and personal qualities such as honesty and tolerance.

The QCA has recently introduced an optional Scheme of Work for citizenship that has been devised to relate directly to the National Curriculum framework.

Where am I? Who am I? (page 155)

Objectives: To know where they live in relation to the European Community; to learn about the wider world and the interdependence of communities within it.

What to do: This is a puzzle with a difference. The parts are named although the children will need to work out where to leave the gaps for sea themselves. We suggest that you have a large and up-to-date map of Europe up on the wall. The European Union publishes maps and other educational material that you may well already have in school as there are periodic mailings of useful material. For more detail consult www.cec.org.uk. Our map showing the 15 EU member states was correct at the time of going to press, but there are currently ten candidate countries preparing for accession in 2004. This sheet asks the children to find out which countries want to join the EU. Ideally, the pieces of the map should be mounted on card (it is best to do this before cutting out). Most Year 5 children should manage the cutting themselves. Obviously we have not been able to include all countries in 'Europe' for space reasons.

Differentiation: You must provide up-to-date atlases, encyclopedias and so on to aid children in assembling the map and finding out about the flags. Photo-enlarging will make the activity easier as will mounting the pieces on card. Mixed-ability pairing is probably the best way of going about this.

Extension: The door is open for any work on the EU that you might wish to undertake. Ask children to find out two or three important facts about each EU country (a possible homework task). Investigate the 'glue' that holds the countries of the EU together. Look at passports, common laws, currency, trade, the European Parliament, and so on. Ask and discuss. *Does the EU have a parliament? Does it have a flag? Does it have an anthem? Does it have a president? Does it have an army?*

My connections (page 156)

Objective: To understand the interdependence of individuals, groups and communities.

What to do: Let children fill the picture frame with a picture of themselves. They can either draw this or use a photograph. Talk about how, although Britain is an island, we are connected both as individuals and a nation with places all over the world. Point out that they may be wearing trainers from Taiwan and a suntan from Spain, have eaten a grapefruit from South Africa for breakfast and played music from the USA on their stereo. Some personal connections can be very close. Direct children to look closely at the illustrations for clues. Instruct them to list places with which they have connections, to say what that connection is and to measure the approximate distance from school to that place. The latter should be done 'as the crow flies' and is best done on a world map using a piece of string or a ruler.

Differentiation: This needs to be an individual activity but some children may need the support of being able to talk about the 'connections'. We suggest small groups but with an adult to help the discussion, as connections may be unique and personal. Finding places on an atlas may also pose a challenge and the group can cooperate in tackling this. You must have high quality atlases for the children to use.

Extension: There must be a plenary session to talk about connections. Mark all the connections on a wall map of the world. Make children aware of how important our connections are, both as a nation (trade, holidays, aid, support in times of trouble) and as individuals (family roots). In multi-ethnic classes the opportunity for encouraging understanding of other places and customs is obvious, but it will be a rare class that does not have personal links that go beyond national boundaries. You might encourage children to find evidence to demonstrate one of their links. They could give short talks to the class, for example 'My holiday in South Africa', 'My granddad in Barbados'.

People with power – your local authority (page 157)

Objective: To have a simple understanding of democratic processes and institutions that support it locally and nationally.

What to do: First, make children aware of the existence of the local authority. Perhaps you could look out of the window at the refuse collectors when they come to your school. *Why do they come? Who pays for them?* Perhaps the children's exercise books have the name of the local authority on them or it may have been painted on the notice board at the school entrance. Children may have seen but not noticed. In order to answer the questions on the sheet you may need to provide some support materials. Telephone directories are useful as they contain details of all the local authority departments and hence clues to the services that they provide. There may be a local Internet site that children could visit to find out local political details. It is as well to check this out first (clearly we cannot provide the answers here). Local authorities provide many services: education, leisure, parks, refuse disposal, vermin extermination, health inspection, local trading checks, planning and architecture, crematoria and cemeteries, social services, road maintenance, housing and so on.

Differentiation: Some children may need to be led by the hand on this activity; local politics is usually a blank in young children's minds. It may help to make this a group task. Let children brainstorm to provide a list of local authority services and provide adult help with finding their way around a telephone directory.

Extension: A visit from a representative of the council should be easy to arrange. A more hands-on approach is to take the children on a walkabout. Show them where the council offices are (a visit to the council chamber can be arranged), point out the presence of local authority depots, offices and services. *How many local authority services and places can you spot on the walk?* For homework children could find out about their council tax (be sensitive).

Feeling is understanding (page 158)

Objectives: To use their imaginations to understand the experiences of others; to care about other people's feelings and to consider other people's needs.

What to do: This is an exercise in empathy. *How does it feel to be somebody else, especially somebody with a physical disability?* The sheet is intended to give children an insight into the problems of blind people and to appreciate the skills that they develop; the Braille sheet is representative only. Hopefully you will have adhesive dots (the coloured kind available in any decent stationers) which the children can use to raise the dots above the surface of the paper.

Differentiation: The task does not require differentiating although there will be differentiation by outcome. Make sure that children have plenty of time to practise using their fingers to feel the bumps.

Extension: Try out Braille for real. Try to obtain a sheet of Braille for the children to handle. *Apart from reading, what other needs might blind people have?* Think about mobility around the school. Ask children to act as mobility officers and inspect the school for hazards. Produce a plan to improve the school so that it would be safer for blind people.

What is important? (page 159)

Objective: To think about and recognise the importance of trust, honesty and respect.

What to do: There are various ways of using this sheet. The most obvious is simply to use it as a focus for class discussion. *What is going on here? What is wrong? Why is it wrong?* Alternatively, you might ask children to redraw one of the cartoons to demonstrate what should happen if people were trustworthy, honest and showed respect for each other. Some children may spot that the titles are actually misnomers – they should be distrust, dishonesty and disrespect!

Differentiation: If this is not used as a whole-class task then children should work in mixed-ability groups of about half a dozen. Ask children to think of examples they know of trust, honesty and respect.

Extension: Ask children to design a poster or TV advertisement (use a storyboard approach) to encourage people to be trustworthy, honest or respectful.

Tolerant people might... (page 160)

Objective: To consider how and why we should demonstrate tolerance and respect for others.

What to do: Children could do this sheet 'cold' with a plenary session to discuss the answers afterwards. Do they understand what being tolerant means? There are no definitive answers to the problems posed in the cartoons and children should understand that being tolerant is not always easy and often involves compromise, which can be quite difficult. For example, *I like silence, you like loud music.* How would the children compromise on that one?

Differentiation: Don't let the writing get in the way of the children's thinking about the issues. One way to tackle this is to put children into mixed-ability groups and let the children appoint a scribe to record the group's answers.

Extension: Ask children to list ways in which they might be more tolerant of other people. You could reverse this and look at the negative side. How many examples of intolerance can they list?

Where am I? Who am I?

● Cut out these countries of Europe. Can you fit the puzzle together correctly? (You will need an atlas.) Mark where you live.

● Put a coloured border around all the countries that belong to the European Union (EU).

● Can you find out which countries want to join the EU?

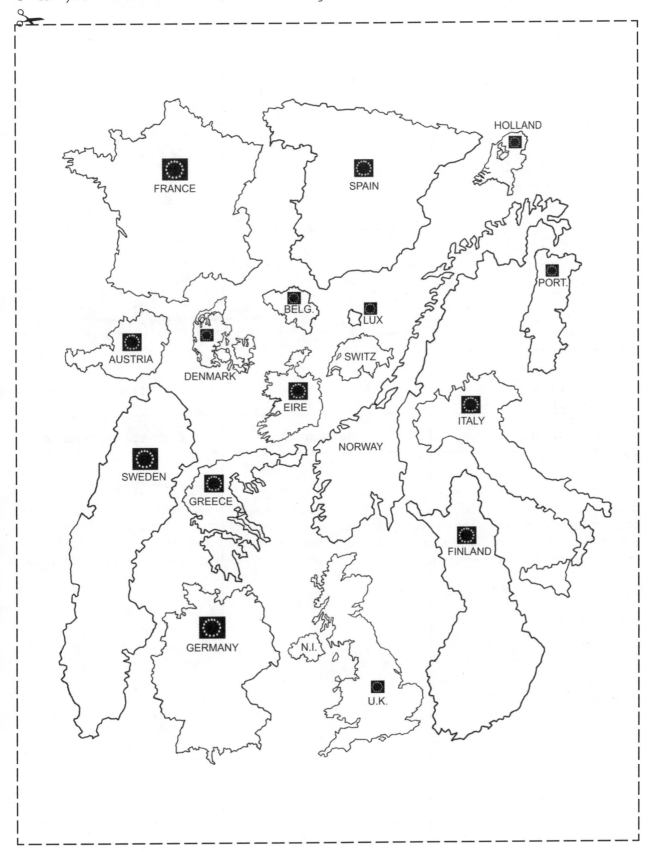

My connections

I have connections with…

Place	Reason	Distance from home

People with power – your local authority

Your **local authority** gets money from a local tax called **council tax** and from the government. It has the **power** and right to do this because Britain is a **democracy**. This means that **councillors**, who run the local authority, must be **elected** by local people. The local authority has a **duty** to use this money to provide local **services**.

● The kind of local authority that you have depends on where you live. Find out about yours (a telephone directory may help).

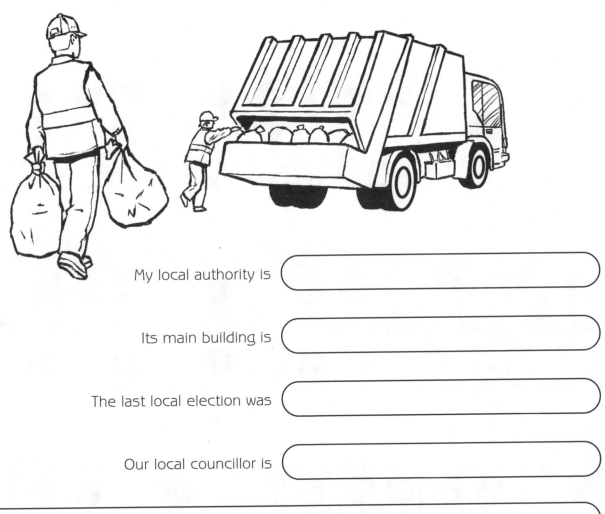

My local authority is

Its main building is

The last local election was

Our local councillor is

Services that my local authority provides	
Service	**Example**
Parks	
Education	

Feeling is understanding

Reading is not always easy but it is even harder when you cannot see. **Braille** was invented as a way of feeling words instead of seeing them. Letters are made from small raised dots on a 2-by-3-grid pattern. The dots can be felt with the fingertips.

● Find out what it is like to do this for yourself. Use sticky circles to raise the dots (in bold) above the others on the paper. Cut out the letters to form your first name. If you need more letters, make them. Try reading without looking. Remember that your dots are much bigger than the real ones.

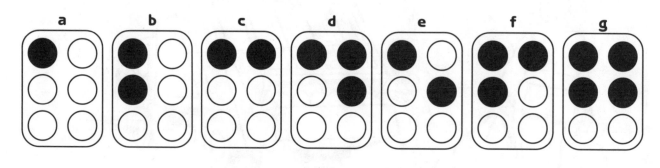

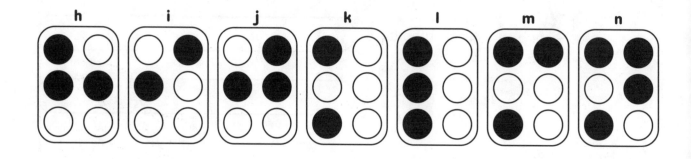

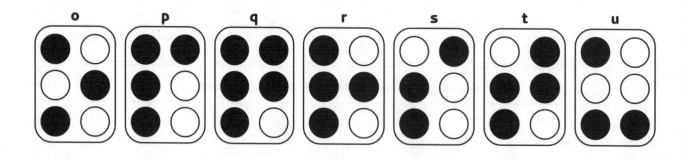

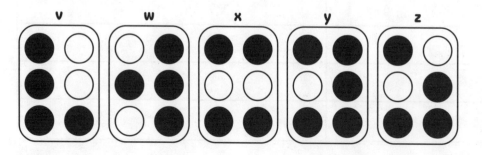

What is important?

Trust

Honesty

Respect

Tolerant people might...

Tolerant people might...

Tolerant people might...

Tolerant people might...